Connected  Mathematics™

D1317343

Prime Time

Factors and Multiples

Teacher's Guide

Glenda Lappan
James T. Fey
William M. Fitzgerald
Susan N. Friel
Elizabeth Difanis Phillips

PEARSON

Prentice
Hall

Needham, Massachusetts
Upper Saddle River, New Jersey

Connected Mathematics™ was developed at Michigan State University with financial support from the Michigan State University Office of the Provost, Computing and Technology, and the College of Natural Science.

This material is based upon work supported by the National Science Foundation under Grant No. MDR 9150217.

This project was supported, in part,
by the
National Science Foundation
Opinions expressed are those of the authors
and not necessarily those of the Foundation

The Michigan State University authors and administration have agreed that all MSU royalties arising from this publication will be devoted to purposes supported by the Department of Mathematics and the MSU Mathematics Education Enrichment Fund.

Photo Acknowledgements: 11 © Brian Baer/UPI/Bettmann; 13 © Ray Massey/Tony Stone Images; 24 © A. Rezny/The Image Works; 26 © Akos Szilvasi/Stock, Boston; 37 © The Bettmann Archive; 41 © John Kelly/Tony Stone Images; 55 © Mike and Carol Werner/Comstock

PEARSON
Prentice
Hall

ISBN 0-13-180780-3
4 5 6 7 8 9 10   07 06 05

The Connected Mathematics Project Staff

Project Directors

James T. Fey
University of Maryland

William M. Fitzgerald
Michigan State University

Susan N. Friel
University of North Carolina at Chapel Hill

Glenda Lappan
Michigan State University

Elizabeth Difanis Phillips
Michigan State University

Project Manager

Kathy Burgis
Michigan State University

Technical Coordinator

Judith Martus Miller
Michigan State University

Collaborating Teachers/Writers

Mary K. Bouck
Portland, Michigan

Jacqueline Stewart
Okemos, Michigan

Curriculum Development Consultants

David Ben-Chaim
Weizmann Institute

Alex Friedlander
Weizmann Institute

Eleanor Geiger
University of Maryland

Jane Mitchell
University of North Carolina at Chapel Hill

Anthony D. Rickard
Alma College

Evaluation Team

Mark Hoover
Michigan State University

Diane V. Lambdin
Indiana University

Sandra K. Wilcox
Michigan State University

Judith S. Zawojewski
National-Louis University

Graduate Assistants

Scott J. Baldridge
Michigan State University

Angie S. Eshelman
Michigan State University

M. Faaiz Gierdien
Michigan State University

Jane M. Keiser
Indiana University

Angela S. Krebs
Michigan State University

James M. Larson
Michigan State University

Ronald Preston
Indiana University

Tat Ming Sze
Michigan State University

Sarah Theule-Lubienski
Michigan State University

Jeffrey J. Wanko
Michigan State University

Field Test Production Team

Katherine Oesterle
Michigan State University

Stacey L. Otto
University of North Carolina at Chapel Hill

Teacher/Assessment Team

Kathy Booth
Waverly, Michigan

Anita Clark
Marshall, Michigan

Theodore Gardella
Bloomfield Hills, Michigan

Yvonne Grant
Portland, Michigan

Linda R. Lobue
Vista, California

Suzanne McGrath
Chula Vista, California

Nancy McIntyre
Troy, Michigan

Linda Walker
Tallahassee, Florida

Software Developer

Richard Burgis
East Lansing, Michigan

Development Center Directors

Nicholas Branca
San Diego State University

Dianne Briars
Pittsburgh Public Schools

Frances R. Curcio
New York University

Perry Lanier
Michigan State University

J. Michael Shaughnessy
Portland State University

Charles Vonder Embse
Central Michigan University

Field Test Coordinators

Michelle Bohan
Queens, New York

Melanie Branca
San Diego, California

Alecia Devantier
Shepherd, Michigan

Jenny Jorgensen
Flint, Michigan

Sandra Kralovec
Portland, Oregon

Sonia Marsalis
Flint, Michigan

William Schaeffer
Pittsburgh, Pennsylvania

Karma Vince
Toledo, Ohio

Virginia Wolf
Pittsburgh, Pennsylvania

Shirel Yaloz
Queens, New York

Student Assistants

Laura Hammond
David Roche
Courtney Stoner
Jovan Trpovski
Julie Valicenti
Michigan State University

Patricia Wagner
Holmes Middle School

Greg Williams
Gundry Elementary School

Lansing

Susan Bissonette
Waverly Middle School

Kathy Booth
Waverly East Intermediate School

Carole Campbell
Waverly East Intermediate School

Gary Gillespie
Waverly East Intermediate School

Denise Kehren
Waverly Middle School

Virginia Larson
Waverly East Intermediate School

Kelly Martin
Waverly Middle School

Laurie Metevier
Waverly East Intermediate School

Craig Paksi
Waverly East Intermediate School

Tony Pecoraro
Waverly Middle School

Helene Rewa
Waverly East Intermediate School

Arnold Stiefel
Waverly Middle School

Portland

Bill Carlton
Portland Middle School

Kathy Dole
Portland Middle School

Debby Flate
Portland Middle School

Yvonne Grant
Portland Middle School

Terry Keusch
Portland Middle School

John Manzini
Portland Middle School

Mary Parker
Portland Middle School

Scott Sandborn
Portland Middle School

Shepherd

Steve Brant
Shepherd Middle School

Marty Brock
Shepherd Middle School

Cathy Church
Shepherd Middle School

Ginny Crandall
Shepherd Middle School

Craig Ericksen
Shepherd Middle School

Natalie Hackney
Shepherd Middle School

Bill Hamilton
Shepherd Middle School

Julie Salisbury
Shepherd Middle School

Sturgis

Sandra Allen
Eastwood Elementary School

Margaret Baker
Eastwood Elementary School

Steven Baker
Eastwood Elementary School

Keith Barnes
Sturgis Middle School

Wilodean Beckwith
Eastwood Elementary School

Darcy Bird
Eastwood Elementary School

Bill Dickey
Sturgis Middle School

Ellen Eisele
Sturgis Middle School

James Hoelscher
Sturgis Middle School

Richard Nolan
Sturgis Middle School

J. Hunter Raiford
Sturgis Middle School

Cindy Sprowl
Eastwood Elementary School

Leslie Stewart
Eastwood Elementary School

Connie Sutton
Eastwood Elementary School

Traverse City

Maureen Bauer
Interlochen Elementary School

Ivanka Berskshire
East Junior High School

Sarah Boehm
Courtade Elementary School

Marilyn Conklin
Interlochen Elementary School

Nancy Crandall
Blair Elementary School

Fran Cullen
Courtade Elementary School

Eric Dreier
Old Mission Elementary School

Lisa Dzierwa
Cherry Knoll Elementary School

Ray Fouch
West Junior High School

Ed Hargis
Willow Hill Elementary School

Richard Henry
West Junior High School

Dessie Hughes
Cherry Knoll Elementary School

Ruthanne Kladder
Oak Park Elementary School

Bonnie Knapp
West Junior High School

Sue Laisure
Sabin Elementary School

Stan Malaski
Oak Park Elementary School

Jody Meyers
Sabin Elementary School

Marsha Myles
East Junior High School

Mary Beth O'Neil
Traverse Heights Elementary School

Jan Palkowski
East Junior High School

Karen Richardson
Old Mission Elementary School

Kristin Sak
Bertha Vos Elementary School

Mary Beth Schmitt
East Junior High School

Mike Schrotenboer
Norris Elementary School

Gail Smith
Willow Hill Elementary School

Karrie Tufts
Eastern Elementary School

Mike Wilson
East Junior High School

Tom Wilson
West Junior High School

Minnesota

Minneapolis

Betsy Ford
Northeast Middle School

New York

East Elmhurst

Allison Clark
Louis Armstrong Middle School

Dorothy Hershey
Louis Armstrong Middle School

J. Lewis McNeece
Louis Armstrong Middle School

Rossana Perez
Louis Armstrong Middle School

Merna Porter
Louis Armstrong Middle School

Marie Turini
Louis Armstrong Middle School

North Carolina

Durham

Everly Broadway
Durham Public Schools

Thomas Carson
Duke School for Children

Mary Hebrank
Duke School for Children

Bill O'Connor
Duke School for Children

Ruth Pershing
Duke School for Children

Peter Reichert
Duke School for Children

Elizabeth City

Rita Banks
Elizabeth City Middle School

Beth Chaundry
Elizabeth City Middle School

Amy Cuthbertson
Elizabeth City Middle School

Deni Dennison
Elizabeth City Middle School

Jean Gray
Elizabeth City Middle School

John McMenamin
Elizabeth City Middle School

Nicollette Nixon
Elizabeth City Middle School

Malinda Norfleet
Elizabeth City Middle School

Joyce O'Neal
Elizabeth City Middle School

Clevie Sawyer
Elizabeth City Middle School

Juanita Shannon
Elizabeth City Middle School

Terry Thorne
Elizabeth City Middle School

Rebecca Wardour
Elizabeth City Middle School

Leora Winslow
Elizabeth City Middle School

Franklinton

Susan Haywood
Franklinton Elementary School

Clyde Melton
Franklinton Elementary School

Louisburg

Lisa Anderson
Terrell Lane Middle School

Jackie Frazier
Terrell Lane Middle School

Pam Harris
Terrell Lane Middle School

Ohio

Toledo

Bonnie Bias
Hawkins Elementary School

Marsha Jackish
Hawkins Elementary School

Lee Jagodzinski
DeVeaux Junior High School

Norma J. King
Old Orchard Elementary School

Margaret McCready
Old Orchard Elementary School

Carmella Morton
DeVeaux Junior High School

Karen C. Rohrs
Hawkins Elementary School

Marie Sahloff
DeVeaux Junior High School

L. Michael Vince
McTigue Junior High School

Brenda D. Watkins
Old Orchard Elementary School

Oregon

Portland

Roberta Cohen
Catlin Gabel School

David Ellenberg
Catlin Gabel School

Sara Normington
Catlin Gabel School

Karen Scholte-Arce
Catlin Gabel School

West Linn

Marge Burack
Wood Middle School

Tracy Wygant
Athey Creek Middle School

Canby

Sandra Kralovec
Ackerman Middle School

Pennsylvania

Pittsburgh

Sheryl Adams
Reizenstein Middle School

Sue Barie
Frick International Studies Academy

Suzie Berry
Frick International Studies Academy

Richard Delgrosso
Frick International Studies Academy

Janet Falkowski
Frick International Studies Academy

Joanne George
Reizenstein Middle School

Harriet Hopper
Reizenstein Middle School

Chuck Jessen
Reizenstein Middle School

Ken Labuskes
Reizenstein Middle School

Barbara Lewis
Reizenstein Middle School

Sharon Mihalich
Reizenstein Middle School

Marianne O'Connor
Frick International Studies Academy

Mark Sammartino
Reizenstein Middle School

Washington

Seattle

Chris Johnson
University Preparatory Academy

Rick Purn
University Preparatory Academy

Contents

Many common and important arithmetic problems involve breaking a whole number into equal-size pieces or finding a number into which a given number will divide evenly. Solving problems like these involves finding factors and multiples. For example:

- A class of 30 students is to be divided into equal-size teams for a school competition. What team sizes are possible?
- Frida and Georgia want to go to the art museum together the next time they both have a day off from work. Frida has a day off every fourth day. Georgia has a day off every fifth day. They both had the day off today. In how many days will they be able to go to the museum?

Solving the first problem involves finding factor pairs of 30. The class can be divided into 2 teams of 15, 3 teams of 10, 5 teams of 6, 6 teams of 5, 10 teams of 3, or 15 teams of 2. One of the most curious and important properties of the whole number system is that the answer to this question depends greatly on the number being divided. For example, if the class had just one more student, it could only be divided into 1 team of 31 or 31 teams of 1.

The second problem involves multiples. We need to find the smallest number that both 4 and 5 are factors of. This number is 20, the least common multiple of 4 and 5. Frida and Georgia can go to the museum in 20 days.

Solving grouping and repeated-actions problems like those above depends on finding factors and multiples of whole numbers. Realizing that some numbers are rich in factors, while other numbers have very few factors is essential for effective problem solving. A primary goal of this unit is to help students learn some new and useful strategies for finding factors and multiples of whole numbers—strategies which they then apply to gain familiarity with prime and composite numbers and to solve real-life problems.

The Mathematics in *Prime Time*

Prime Time addresses the basics of number theory: factors, multiples, prime and composite numbers, even and odd numbers, square numbers, greatest common factors, and least common multiples. The concepts of factor and multiple are interdependent. If A is a factor of B, then B is a multiple of A. This means that we can find a number C such that the product of A and C equals B, that is, $A \times C = B$. From this we see that factors always come in pairs.

Through their work in these investigations, your students discover the Fundamental Theorem of Arithmetic. This theorem states that, except for order, every whole number can be written as the product of primes in exactly one way. For example, the number 120 can be written as $2 \times 2 \times 2 \times 3 \times 5$. Although you can switch the order of the factors—for example, you can write $2 \times 3 \times 2 \times 5 \times 2$—every prime product string for 120 will have three 2s, one 3, and one 5.

The Fundamental Theorem of Arithmetic helps us to see why 1 is not a prime number. In essence, the theorem states that a whole number can be identified uniquely by its prime factorization. That is, each whole number corresponds to a unique prime factorization, and each prime factorization corresponds to a unique whole number. If 1 were a prime number, this would not be true. Any string of primes could be extended with an unlimited number of 1s.

Mathematical and Problem-Solving Goals

Prime Time **was created to help students**

- Understand the relationships among factors, multiples, divisors, and products
- Recognize that factors come in pairs
- Link area and dimensions of rectangles with products and factors
- Recognize numbers as prime or composite and as odd or even based on their factors
- Use factors and multiples to explain some numerical facts of everyday life
- Develop strategies for finding factors and multiples of whole numbers
- Recognize that a number can be written in exactly one way as a product of primes (Fundamental Theorem of Arithmetic)
- Recognize situations in which problems can be solved by finding factors and multiples
- Develop a variety of strategies—such as building a physical model, making a table or list, and solving a simpler problem—to solve problems involving factors and multiples

The overall goal of Connected Mathematics is to help students develop sound mathematical habits. Through their work in this and other number units, students learn important questions to ask themselves about any situation that can be represented and modeled mathematically, such as: *What is a factor of a number? How can factors be found? Do all numbers have factors? How can factor and multiple concepts be shown physically with tiles and rectangles? What does it mean to say that a number is prime? Why must a factor string be unique? How can these ideas relate to the physical world? What are common factors and common multiples? How do these concepts further mathematical understanding?*

Investigation 1: The Factor Game

The Factor Game engages students in a friendly contest in which winning strategies involve distinguishing between numbers with many factors and numbers with few factors. Students are then guided through an analysis of game strategies and introduced to the definitions of *prime* and *composite numbers.* The ACE questions are rich in connections to situations in which factors, multiples, and prime numbers are significant.

Investigation 2: The Product Game

In the Product Game, students find products of factors. Although students develop strategies to win the game, the focus is on basic multiplication facts. Students then create their own games by selecting factors, determining products, and choosing appropriate dimensions for their game boards.

Investigation 3: Factor Pairs

Students use square tiles to make all possible rectangles to represent the numbers 1 through 30. Finding rectangles with a given area helps students to visualize whole numbers and to list factor pairs. The rectangles also provide a foundation to discuss how many factors must be checked to find all the factor pairs of a number. Connecting factor pairs to area previews the study of measurement in the *Covering and Surrounding* unit. Square tiles are then used to model even and odd numbers. When students have generalized the patterns, they use the models to prove conjectures about the sums and products of odd and even numbers.

Investigation 4: Common Factors and Multiples

Real-life situations are used to motivate student interest in common factors and common multiples. The concepts of least common multiple and greatest common factor, though not formally introduced, are used naturally throughout the problems and in the ACE section. The context of the problems and questions helps make clear whether a solution involves finding a common multiple, a common factor, the least common multiple, or the greatest common factor.

Investigation 5: Factorizations

Finding longer and longer factor strings of a number leads students to discover the Fundamental Theorem of Arithmetic: a whole number can be factored into a product of primes in exactly one way. Factor trees are used as a systematic way of finding the prime factorization of a number. The last problem in the investigation helps students use prime factorizations to find the greatest common factor and least common multiple of two or more numbers. The discussion of why 1 is not a prime occurs in the ACE section.

Investigation 6: The Locker Problem

This investigation concludes the unit with a look at a fanciful problem. The Locker Problem provides an excellent way to summarize the unit and involves all the ideas about the multiplicative structure of numbers developed in the rest of the unit. Students organize data, look for patterns, and solve problems involving factors and multiples.

The ideas in *Prime Time* build on and connect to several big ideas in other Connected Mathematics units.

Big Idea	Prior Work	Future Work
determining the factors of whole numbers; finding the greatest common factor of two numbers	learning and applying multiplication and division facts; applying the division algorithm (*elementary school*)	performing arithmetic operations with fractions (*Bits and Pieces I & II*); comparing, scaling, and testing for similarity (*Stretching and Shrinking, Comparing and Scaling*); factoring algebraic expressions (*Say It With Symbols*)
generating multiples of numbers; finding the least common multiple of two numbers	learning and applying multiplication facts; counting by 2s, 3s, etc. (*elementary school*)	understanding decimal numbers and the concept of place value (*Bits and Pieces I & II, Comparing and Scaling*); identifying and analyzing patterns in the products of two numbers (*Covering and Surrounding, Variables and Patterns, Moving Straight Ahead, Say It With Symbols*)
determining factorizations, including the prime factorization, of a whole number	learning and applying multiplication and division facts; testing numbers for divisibility (*elementary school*)	finding the LCM in order to find common denominators for fractions and ratios (*Bits and Pieces I & II, Com-paring and Scaling*); studying patterns in multiplicative relationships to develop algorithms for finding area, surface area, and volume of figures (*Covering and Surrounding, Filling and Wrapping*); identifying irrational numbers (*Looking for Pythagoras*); studying exponential relationships (*Growing, Growing, Growing, …*); developing and applying counting strategies (*Clever Counting*)
classifying numbers as prime or composite, as even or odd, and as abundant, deficient, or perfect	applying multiplication, addition, and division facts; comparing positive whole numbers (*elementary school*)	classifying numbers as positive or negative (*Accentuate the Negative*) and as rational or irrational (*Looking for Pythagoras*); classifying relationships as linear, quadratic, or exponential (*Variables and Patterns; Moving Straight Ahead; Thinking with Mathematical Models; Growing, Growing, Growing, … ; Frogs, Fleas, and Painted Cubes; Say It With Symbols*)

Materials

For students

- Labsheets (You can laminate game boards for repeated use.)
- Calculators
- Paper clips
- Colored chips (about 12 each of 2 colors per pair)
- Colored pens, pencils, or markers
- Square tiles (about 30 per student)
- Grid paper (provided as a blackline master)
- Scissors
- Tape
- Blank transparencies and transparency markers (optional)

For the teacher

- 12 signs with an open locker on one side and a closed locker on the other (optional; provided as blackline masters)
- Transparencies (optional)
- Transparency markers

Technology

Connected Mathematics was developed with the belief that calculators should always be available and that students should decide when to use them. For this reason, we do not designate specific problems as "calculator problems." The calculations in *Prime Time* involve only simple arithmetic, so nonscientific calculators are adequate.

Resources

For students

Henry, Boyd. *Every Number Is Special*. Palo Alto, Calif.: Dale Seymour Publications, 1985.

Wells, David. *The Penguin Dictionary of Curious and Interesting Numbers*. New York: Penguin Books, 1986.

For teachers

Bezuszka, Stanley and Margaret Kenney. *Number Treasury*. Palo Alto, Calif.: Dale Seymour Publications, 1982.

This pacing chart gives estimates of the class time required for each investigation and assessment piece. Shaded rows indicate opportunities for assessment.

Investigations and Assessments	Class Time
1 The Factor Game	3 days
2 The Product Game	5 days
3 Factor Pairs	4 days
Quiz A	1 day
Check-Up 1	1/2 day
4 Common Factors and Multiples	3 days
5 Factorizations	4 days
Quiz B	1 day
Check-Up 2	1/2 day
6 The Locker Problem	2 days
Self-Assessment	Take home
The Unit Test	1 day
The Unit Project	Take home

Vocabulary

The following words and concepts are introduced and used in *Prime Time*. Concepts in the left column are those that are essential for student understanding of this and future units. The Descriptive Glossary gives descriptions of these and other words used in *Prime Time*.

Essential

common factor

common multiple

composite number

even number

exponent

factor

multiple

odd number

prime factorization

prime number

proper factor

Nonessential

abundant number

divisor

deficient number

Fundamental Theorem of Arithmetic

perfect number

relatively prime numbers

square number

Embedded Assessment

Opportunities for informal assessment of student progress are embedded throughout *Prime Time* in the problems, the ACE questions, and the Mathematical Reflections. Suggestions for observing as students discover and explore mathematical ideas, for probing to guide their progress in developing concepts and skills, and for questioning to determine their level of understanding can be found in the *Launch, Explore,* or *Summarize* sections of all investigation problems. Some examples:

- Investigation 5, Problem 5.1 *Launch* (page 57a) provides help for you in guiding students to develop systematic ways for writing factor strings.
- Investigation 2, Problem 2.2 *Explore* (page 25c) explains why it is important that students understand the need to consider the relationship between the number of products and the size of the Product Game boards they are designing.
- Investigation 3, Problem 3.1 *Summarize* (page 35a) suggests ways to determine whether students understand that squares are rectangles and also points out that it is not important to bring this idea to closure at this time.

ACE Assignments

An ACE (Applications—Connections—Extensions) section appears at the end of each investigation. To help you assign ACE questions, a list of assignment choices is given in the margin next to the reduced student page for each problem. Each list indicates the ACE questions that students should be able to answer after they complete the problem.

Partner Quizzes

Two quizzes, which may be used after Investigations 3 and 5, are provided with *Prime Time.* These quizzes are designed to be completed by pairs of students with the opportunity for revision based on teacher feedback. You will find the quizzes and their answer keys in the Assessment Resources section. As an alternative to the quizzes provided, you can construct your own quizzes by combining questions from the Question Bank, the quizzes, and unassigned ACE questions.

Check-Ups

Two check-ups, which may be used after Investigations 3 and 5, are provided for use as quick quizzes or as warm-up activities. Check-ups are designed for students to complete individually. You will find the check-ups and their answer keys in the Assessment Resources section.

Question Bank

A Question Bank provides additional questions you can use for homework, review, or quizzes. You will find the Question Bank and its answer key in the Assessment Resources section.

Notebook/Journal

Students should have notebooks to record and organize their work. In the notebooks will be their journals, along with sections for vocabulary, homework, and quizzes and check-ups. In their journals, students can take notes, solve investigation problems, record their mathematical reflections, and write down ideas for their unit projects. You should assess student journals for completeness rather than correctness; journals should be seen as "safe" places where students can try out their thinking. A Notebook Checklist and a Self-Assessment are provided in the Assessment Resources section. The Notebook Checklist helps students organize their notebooks. The Self-Assessment guides students as they review their notebooks to determine which ideas they have mastered and which ideas they still need to work on.

The Unit Project: My Special Number

As a final assessment in *Prime Time* you may administer the Unit Test or assign the Unit Project, My Special Number. The project is introduced at the beginning of the unit, when students are asked to choose a number and to write several things about it in their journals. As students complete the investigations, they are asked to write new information about their numbers in their journals. The project is formally assigned at the end of the unit. Students are asked to use all the concepts they have learned in *Prime Time* to create a project highlighting their number. A scoring rubric and samples of student work are given in the Assessment Resources section.

The Unit Test

As a final assessment in *Prime Time*, you may assign the Unit Project or administer the Unit Test. The Unit Test focuses on factors, the relationship between factor pairs and rectangle shapes, and properties of odd and even numbers.

Introducing Your Students to *Prime Time*

One way to introduce *Prime Time* is to ask your students to brainstorm about the ways they use numbers every day. Tell your students that, in *Prime Time*, they will study whole numbers.

Explain that there are many important and interesting questions that involve whole numbers. Refer students to the three questions posed on the opening page of the student edition. You may want to have a class discussion about these questions, but do not worry about finding the "correct" answers at this time. Each question is posed again in the investigations, at the time when students have learned the mathematical concepts required to answer it. Ask your students to keep these questions in mind as they work through the investigations and to think about how they might use the ideas they are learning to help them determine the answers.

After you discuss the questions, refer students to page 5, where the unit project is introduced.

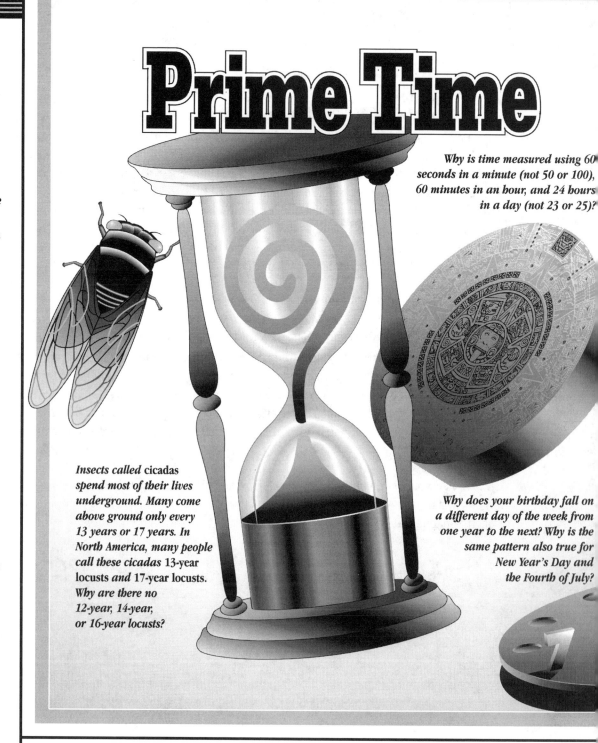

Prime Time

Why is time measured using 60 seconds in a minute (not 50 or 100), 60 minutes in an hour, and 24 hours in a day (not 23 or 25)?

Insects called cicadas spend most of their lives underground. Many come above ground only every 13 years or 17 years. In North America, many people call these cicadas 13-year locusts and 17-year locusts. Why are there no 12-year, 14-year, or 16-year locusts?

Why does your birthday fall on a different day of the week from one year to the next? Why is the same pattern also true for New Year's Day and the Fourth of July?

Everyone uses numbers. Think about the ways you can use them—for counting, for measuring, for making decisions. Numbers help you communicate, find information, use technology, and make purchases. Numbers also can help you think about situations like those on the opposite page.

Whole numbers have interesting properties and structures you may not have thought about before. Some numbers can be divided by many numbers, while others can be divided by only a few. In *Prime Time,* you will learn how to use these ideas about the structure of numbers to explain some curious patterns and to solve some interesting problems including the three on the opposite page.

Mathematical Highlights

The Mathematical Highlights page was designed to provide information to students and to parents and other family members. This page gives students a preview of the activities and problems in *Prime Time*. As they work through the unit, students can refer back to the Mathematical Highlights page to review what they have learned and to preview what is still to come. This page also tells parents and other family members what mathematical ideas and activities will be covered as the class works through *Prime Time*.

Mathematical Highlights

In *Prime Time* you will explore important properties of whole numbers, especially those related to multiplication and division. The unit should help you to

- Understand relationships among factors, multiples, divisors, and products;

- Recognize and use properties of prime and composite numbers, even and odd numbers, and square numbers;

- Link area and dimensions of rectangles with products and factors;

- Develop strategies for finding factors and multiples, least common multiples, and greatest common factors;

- Recognize and use the fact that every whole number can be written in exactly one way as a product of primes;

- Use factors and multiples to solve problems and to explain some numerical facts of everyday life; and

- Develop a variety of strategies for solving problems—building models, making lists and tables, drawing diagrams, and solving simpler problems.

As you work on the problems of this unit, get in the habit of asking questions about situations that involve whole numbers and relationships: *What are the factors of given numbers and how can those factors be found? What common factors and common multiples do the numbers have? What do the factors and multiples of the numbers tell about the situations in which they occur?*

My Special Number

Many people have a number they find interesting. Choose a whole number between 10 and 100 that you especially like.

In your journal

- record your number
- explain why you chose that number
- list three or four mathematical things about your number
- list three or four connections you can make between your number and your world

As you work through the investigations in *Prime Time*, you will learn lots of things about numbers. Think about how these new ideas apply to your special number, and add any new information about your number to your journal. You may want to designate one or two "special number" pages in your journal, where you can record this information. At the end of the unit, your teacher will ask you to find an interesting way to report to the class about your special number.

Introducing the Unit Project

The final assessment for *Prime Time*, the My Special Number project, is introduced on this page and formally assigned at the end of the unit. Here students are asked to choose a number between 10 and 100 and to write several things they already know about it. Throughout the unit, students are reminded to use the concepts they are learning to write more information about their special numbers. At the end of the unit, students are asked to create projects highlighting their numbers.

You can ask students to choose their special number when you introduce the unit. You may want set aside a few minutes of class time for students to write about their numbers. Some teachers have found it useful to have students designate one or two "special number pages" in their journals to record information about their numbers.

See page 65 for information about assigning the project. To help you assess the project, see page 87 of the Assessment Resources section. Here you will find a possible scoring rubric and samples of student projects. Each sample is followed by a teacher's comments about assessing the project.

The Investigations

The teaching materials for each investigation consist of three parts: an overview, the student pages with teaching outlines, and the detailed notes for teaching the investigation.

The overview of each investigation includes brief descriptions of the problems, the mathematical and problem-solving goals of the investigation, and a list of necessary materials.

Essential information for teaching the investigation is provided in the margins around the student pages. The "At a Glance" overviews are brief outlines of the Launch, Explore, and Summarize phases of each problem for reference as you work with the class. To help you assign homework, a list of "Assignment Choices" is provided next to each problem. Wherever space permits, answers to problems, follow-ups, ACE questions, and Mathematical Reflections appear next to the appropriate student pages.

The Teaching the Investigation section follows the student pages and is the heart of the Connected Mathematics curriculum. This section describes in detail the Launch, Explore, and Summarize phases for each problem. It includes all the information needed for teaching, along with suggestions for guiding the discussion. Use this section to prepare lessons and as needed while teaching an investigation.

Assessment Resources

The Assessment Resources section contains blackline masters and answer keys for quizzes, check-ups, and the Question Bank. It also provides guidelines for assessing the unit project and other important student work. Samples of student work, along with a teacher's comments about how each sample was assessed, will help you to evaluate your students' efforts. Blackline masters for the Notebook Checklist and the Self-Assessment support student self-evaluation, an important aspect of assessment in the Connected Mathematics curriculum.

Blackline Masters

The Blackline Masters section includes masters for all labsheets and transparencies. Blackline masters of grid paper and of open and closed locker doors (for Problem 6.1) are also provided.

Additional Practice

Practice pages for each investigation offer additional problems for students who need more practice with the basic concepts developed in the investigations as well as some continual review of earlier concepts.

Descriptive Glossary

The Descriptive Glossary provides descriptions and examples of the key concepts in *Prime Time*. These descriptions are not intended to be formal definitions, but are meant to give you an idea of how students might make sense of these important concepts.

The Factor Game

The purpose of this investigation is twofold: to help students determine whether a given number has many or only a few factors and to show how this property of numbers is useful for problem solving. Problem 1.1, Playing the Factor Game, engages students in a friendly contest in which winning strategies involve recognizing the difference between prime numbers and composite numbers. Problem 1.2, Playing to Win the Factor Game, guides students through an analysis of Factor Game strategies and introduces the definitions of prime and composite numbers. The ACE questions are rich in connections to situations in which factors, multiples, divisors, products, and prime numbers are significant.

Mathematical and Problem-Solving Goals

- **To classify numbers as prime or composite**

- **To recognize that some numbers are rich in factors, while others have few factors**

- **To recognize that factors come in pairs and that once one factor is found, another can also be found**

- **To discover the connection between dividing and finding factors of a number**

Materials		
Problem	**For students**	**For the teacher**
All	Calculators, colored pens, pencils, or markers	Transparencies 1.1 to 1.2B (optional), colored transparency markers
1.1	Labsheet 1.1 (1 per pair)	
1.2	Labsheet 1.2 (1 per student; optional)	

Student Pages 6–16   **Teaching the Investigation 16a–16e**

Playing the Factor Game

Grouping: Pairs

Launch

- Review the definition of factor.

- Introduce the Factor Game by playing a game against your class.

Explore

- Have students play the Factor Game two or three times with a partner.

- As they are playing the game, ask students to think about what the best first move might be.

Summarize

- Ask students to share the ideas they have discovered with the class.

Assignment Choices

ACE questions 1–9 and 14

INVESTIGATION

The Factor Game

Today Jamie is 12 years old. Jamie has three younger cousins: Cam, Emilio, and Ester. They are 2, 3, and 8 years old respectively. The following mathematical sentences show that Jamie is

6 times as old as Cam, 4 times as old as Emilio, and $1\frac{1}{2}$ times as old as Ester

$$12 = 6 \times 2 \qquad\qquad 12 = 4 \times 3 \qquad\qquad 12 = 1\frac{1}{2} \times 8$$

Notice that each of the whole numbers 2, 3, 4, and 6 can be multiplied by another whole number to get 12. We call 2, 3, 4, and 6 *whole number factors* or *whole number divisors* of 12. Although 8 is a whole number, it is not a whole number factor of 12, since we cannot multiply it by another whole number to get 12. To save time, we will simply use the word **factor** to refer to whole number factors.

1.1 Playing the Factor Game

The Factor Game is a two-person game in which players find factors of numbers on a game board. To play the game you will need Labsheet 1.1 and colored pens, pencils, or markers.

Problem 1.1

Play the Factor Game several times with a partner. Take turns making the first move. Look for moves that give the best scores. In your journal, record any strategies you find that help you to win.

Problem 1.1 Follow-Up

Talk with your partner about the games you played. Be prepared to tell the class about a good idea you discoved for playing the game well.

The Factor Game

1	2	3	4	5
6	7	8	9	10
11	12	13	14	15
16	17	18	19	20
21	22	23	24	25
26	27	28	29	30

Factor Game Rules

1. Player A chooses a number on the game board and circles it.

2. Using a different color, Player B circles all the proper factors of Player A's number. The **proper factors** of a number are all the factors of that number, except the number itself. For example, the proper factors of 12 are 1, 2, 3, 4, and 6. Although 12 is a factor of itself, it is not a proper factor.

3. Player B circles a new number, and Player A circles all the factors of the number that are not already circled.

4. The players take turns choosing numbers and circling factors.

5. If a player circles a number that has no factors left that have not been circled, that player loses a turn and does not get the points for the number circled.

6. The game ends when there are no numbers remaining with uncircled factors.

7. Each player adds the numbers that are circled with his or her color. The player with the greater total is the winner.

A sample game is shown on the following pages.

Sample Game

The first column describes the moves the players make. The other columns show the game board and score after each move.

Action	Game Board	Score	
		Cathy	**Keiko**
Cathy circles 24. Keiko circles 1, 2, 3, 4, 6, 8, and 12—the proper factors of 24.	The Factor Game (1) (2) (3) (4) 5 (6) 7 (8) 9 10 11 (12) 13 14 15 16 17 18 19 20 21 22 23 (24) 25 26 27 28 29 30	24	36
Keiko circles 28. Cathy circles 7 and 14—the factors of 28 that are not already circled.	The Factor Game (1) (2) (3) (4) 5 (6) (7) (8) 9 10 11 (12) 13 (14) 15 16 17 18 19 20 21 22 23 (24) 25 26 27 (28) 29 30	24 21	36 28
Cathy circles 27. Keiko circles 9—the only factor of 27 that is not already circled.	The Factor Game (1) (2) (3) (4) 5 (6) (7) (8) (9) 10 11 (12) 13 (14) 15 16 17 18 19 20 21 22 23 (24) 25 26 (27) (28) 29 30	24 21 27	36 28 9
Keiko circles 30. Cathy circles 5, 10, and 15—the factors of 30 that are not already circled.	The Factor Game (1) (2) (3) (4) (5) (6) (7) (8) (9) (10) 11 (12) 13 (14) (15) 16 17 18 19 20 21 22 23 (24) 25 26 (27) (28) 29 (30)	24 21 27 30	36 28 9 30
Cathy circles 25. All the factors of 25 are circled. Cathy loses a turn and does not receive any points for this turn.	The Factor Game (1) (2) (3) (4) (5) (6) (7) (8) (9) (10) 11 (12) 13 (14) (15) 16 17 18 19 20 21 22 23 (24) (25) 26 (27) (28) 29 (30)	24 21 27 30	36 28 9 30

continued		Cathy	Keiko
Keiko circles 26. Cathy circles 13—the only factor of 26 that is not circled.	The Factor Game ① ② ③ ④ ⑤ ⑥ ⑦ ⑧ ⑨ ⑩ 11 ⑫ ⑬ ⑭ ⑮ 16 17 18 19 20 21 22 23 ㉔ ㉕ ㉖ ㉗ ㉘ 29 ㉚	24 21 27 30 13	36 28 9 30 26
Keiko circles 22. Cathy circles 11—the only factor of 22 that is not circled.	The Factor Game ① ② ③ ④ ⑤ ⑥ ⑦ ⑧ ⑨ ⑩ ⑪ ⑫ ⑬ ⑭ ⑮ 16 17 18 19 20 21 ㉒ 23 ㉔ ㉕ ㉖ ㉗ ㉘ 29 ㉚	24 21 27 30 13 11	36 28 9 30 26 22
No numbers remain with uncircled factors. Keiko wins the game.	The Factor Game ① ② ③ ④ ⑤ ⑥ ⑦ ⑧ ⑨ ⑩ ⑪ ⑫ ⑬ ⑭ ⑮ 16 17 18 19 20 21 ㉒ 23 ㉔ ㉕ ㉖ ㉗ ㉘ 29 ㉚	24 21 27 30 13 11	36 28 9 30 26 22
	Total	**126**	**151**

Investigation 1: The Factor Game 9

1.2

Playing to Win the Factor Game

Grouping: Individuals, then Pairs

Launch

- Explain to the class that you want to analyze every possible first move to determine which are "good moves" and which are "bad moves."

- Help your class create a table for analyzing first moves in the Factor Game.

Explore

- Allow students to work alone on their tables, and then to work in pairs to compare and complete their tables.

- Have students work with their partners to complete Problem 1.2 and Problem 1.2 Follow-Up.

Summarize

- Hold a class discussion in which students share their solutions with the class.

- Ask students to record the results of the class discussion in their journals.

Assignment Choices

ACE questions 10–13, 15–21, and unassigned choices from the previous problem

---

1.2 Playing to Win the Factor Game

Did you find that some numbers are better than others to pick for the first move in the Factor Game? For example, if you pick 22, you get 22 points and your opponent gets only $1 + 2 + 11 = 14$ points. However, if you pick 18, you get 18 points, and your opponent gets $1 + 2 + 3 + 6 + 9 = 21$ points!

Make a table of all the possible first moves (numbers from 1 to 30) you could make. For each move, list the proper factors, and record the scores you and your opponent would receive. Your table might start like this:

First move	Proper factors	My score	Opponent's score
1	none	lose a turn	0
2	1	2	1
3	1	3	1
4	1, 2	4	3

Problem 1.2

Use your list to figure out the best and worst first moves.

A. What is the best first move? Why?

B. What is the worst first move? Why?

C. Look for other patterns in your list. Describe an interesting pattern that you find.

Problem 1.2 Follow-Up

1. List all the first moves that allow your opponent to score only one point. These kinds of numbers have a special name. They are called **prime numbers.**
2. Are all prime numbers good first moves? (A number is a good first move if the player picking the number scores more points than his or her opponent.) Explain your answer.
3. List all the first moves that allow your opponent to score more than one point. These kinds of numbers also have a special name. They are called **composite numbers.**
4. Are composite numbers good first moves? Explain your answer.
5. Which first move would make you lose a turn? Why?

Answers to Problem 1.2

A. 29; It gives you the largest point advantage over your opponent.

B. 24 and 30; Your opponent gets 12 points more than you get.

C. See page 16d for some patterns that students have noticed.

Did you know?

The search for prime numbers has fascinated mathematicians for a very long time. We know that there are an infinite number of primes, but we have no way to predict which numbers are prime. We must test each number to see if it has exactly two factors—1 and itself. For very large numbers, this testing takes a long time, even with the help of a supercomputer that can perform 16 billion calculations per second!

In 1994, David Slowinski, a computer scientist at Cray Research, found a prime number with 258,716 digits. The previous record holder had 227,832 digits. Large prime numbers are of special importance in coding systems for transmitting secret information. The difficulty of breaking these codes depends on the difficulty of factoring a composite number with 100 or more digits into prime factors with at least 50 digits. Computer programmers think that such a problem would require over a billion years on the largest imaginable supercomputer.

Adapted from Phillips et al., *Addenda Series, Grades 5–8: Patterns and Functions* (Reston, Va.: National Council of Teachers of Mathematics, 1991), p. 21, and information provided by Cray Resear

Answers to Problem 1.2 Follow-Up

1. 2, 3, 5, 7, 11, 13, 17, 19, 23, and 29

2. yes; All primes are good first moves because the second player gets only one point. Large primes are the best first moves.

3. 4, 6, 8, 9, 10, 12, 14, 15, 16, 18, 20, 21, 22, 24, 25, 26, 27, 28, and 30

4. Some composite numbers are good first moves and others are not; it depends on the sum of the factors. For example, 30 is a bad first move because the second player gets 42 points; 25 is not as bad because the second player gets only 6 points.

5. 1; There are no factors for the other player to choose.

Answers

Applications

1. Divide 24 by 6 to get 4, so $6 \times 4 = 24$.

2. 4

3. 9

4. 8

5. Although $7.5 \times 6 = 45$, 7.5 is not a whole number and therefore not considered a factor. This problem and problem 9 give you a chance to check whether students understand that we are concerned with whole number factors only.

6. 8

7. 11

8. 4

9. Although 10.0909 . . . $\times 11 = 111$, 10.0909 . . . is not a whole number and therefore not considered a factor.

10a. See page 16d.

10b. 31, 37, 41, 43, and 47

As you work on these ACE questions, use your calculator whenever you need it.

Applications

1. Your opponent in the Factor Game claims that 6 is a factor of 24. How can you check to see whether this is correct?

2. What factor is paired with 6 to give 24?

3. What factor is paired with 5 to give 45?

4. What factor is paired with 3 to give 24?

5. What factor is paired with 6 to give 45?

6. What factor is paired with 6 to give 48?

7. What factor is paired with 11 to give 121?

8. What factor is paired with 12 to give 48?

9. What factor is paired with 11 to give 111?

10. The Factor Game can be played on a 49-board, which contains whole numbers from 1 to 49.

The Factor Game						
1	2	3	4	5	6	7
8	9	10	11	12	13	14
15	16	17	18	19	20	21
22	23	24	25	26	27	28
29	30	31	32	33	34	35
36	37	38	39	40	41	42
43	44	45	46	47	48	49

a. Extend your table for analyzing first moves on a 30-factor game board to include all the numbers on a 49-board.

b. What new primes do you find?

11. Suppose your opponent has the first move on the 49-board and chooses 49.

    a. How many points does your opponent score for this round?

    b. How many points do you score for this round?

12. What is the best first move on a 49-board? Why?

13. What is the worst first move on a 49-board? Why?

14. **a.** What do you get when you use your calculator to divide 84 by 14? What does this tell you about 14 and 84?

    b. What do you get when you use your calculator to divide 84 by 15? What does this tell you about 15 and 84?

15. Use the ideas from this investigation to list at least five facts about the number 30.

16. What is my number?

    Clue 1 My number has two digits, and both digits are even.

    Clue 2 The sum of my number's digits is 10.

    Clue 3 My number has 4 as a factor.

    Clue 4 The difference between the two digits of my number is 6.

Connections

17. A class of 30 students is to be divided into equal-size groups. What group sizes are possible?

18. Long ago, people observed the sun rising and setting over and over at about equal intervals. They decided to use the amount of time between two sunrises as the length of a day. They divided the day into 24 hours. Use what you know about factors to answer these questions:

    a. Why is 24 a more convenient choice than 23 or 25?

    b. If you were to select a number different from 24 to represent the hours in a day what number would you choose? Why?

11a. 49

11b. 8

12. 47; It is the largest prime number on the board.

13. 48; The second player gets 76 points—28 more points than the first player.

14a. 6; Since the result is a whole number, 14 is a factor of 84.

14b. 5.6; Since the result is not a whole number, 15 is not a factor of 84.

15. Possible answers: 30 is an even number. 30 is a composite number. The factors of 30 are 1, 2, 3, 5, 6, 10, 15, and 30. The proper factors of 30 are 1, 2, 3, 5, 6, 10, and 15. The sum of the digits of 30 is 3 + 0 = 3. The difference between the two digits of 30 is 3 − 0 = 3

16. The numbers with two even digits (Clue 1) that add to 10 (Clue 2) are 28, 46, 64, and 82. Of these numbers, 4 is a factor (Clue 3) of 28 and 64. Of these two numbers, only 28 has digits with a difference of 6 (Clue 4). The number is 28.

Connections

17. 30 groups of 1, 15 groups of 2, 10 groups of 3, 6 groups of 5, 5 groups of 6, 3 groups of 10, 2 groups of 15, and 1 group of 30

18a. Since 24 has many factors, it can be divided into many equal parts. Since 23 is prime, it cannot be subdivided. The only proper factors of 25 are 1 and 5, so it can only be subdivided into 5 groups of 5.

18b. Possible answers: 12, 18, 20, 28, 30, 32; These numbers have many factors.

Extensions

19a. 117 = 50 + 25 + 20 + 10 + 5 + 4 + 2 + 1

19b. 57 = 33 + 11 + 9 + 3 + 1

19c. 97, the largest prime number less than 100

20a. See below right.

20b. *Abundant* means "more then enough," which is appropriate since the sum of an abundant number's factors is more than the number. *Deficient* means "not enough," which is appropriate since the sum of a deficient number's factors is less than the number. *Perfect* means "exactly right," which is appropriate because the sum of a perfect number's factors is equal to the number.

20c. abundant

20d. deficient

21a. 15 = 8 + 4 + 2 + 1; Your opponent scores one fewer point.

21b. 3 = 2 + 1; Your opponent scores one fewer point.

21c. See page 16e.

Extensions

19. Suppose you and a friend decide to use a 100-board to play the Factor Game.
  a. What would your score be if your friend chose 100 as the first move?
  b. What would your score be if your friend chose 99 as the first move?
  c. What is the best first move?

20. The sum of the proper factors of a number may be greater than, less than, or equal to the number. Ancient mathematicians used this idea to classify numbers as **abundant, deficient,** and **perfect.** Each whole number greater than 1 falls into one of these three categories.
  a. Draw and label three circles as shown below. The numbers 12, 15, and 6 have been placed in the appropriate circles. Use your factor list to figure out what each label means. Then, write each whole number from 2 to 30 in the correct circle.

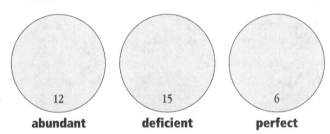

| abundant | deficient | perfect |

  b. Do the labels seem appropriate? Why or why not?
  c. In which circle would 36 belong?
  d. In which circle would 55 belong?

21. **a.** If you choose 16 as a first move in the Factor Game, how many points does your opponent get? How does your opponent's score for this turn compare to yours?
  b. If you choose 4 as a first move, how many points does your opponent get? How does your opponent's score for this turn compare to yours?
  c. Find some other numbers that have the same pattern of scoring as 4 and 16. These numbers could be called **near-perfect numbers.** Why do you think this name fits?

20a.

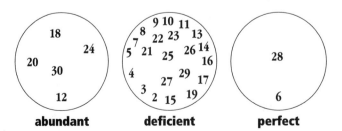

Did you know?

Is there a largest perfect number? Mathematicians have been trying for hundreds of years to find the answer to this question. You might like to know that the next largest perfect number, after 6 and 28, is 496!

1. Prime numbers are good first moves. Since the only proper factor of a prime number is 1, your opponent scores only 1 point. Large prime numbers are the best moves. For example, 29 gives you 29 points and your opponent only 1 point.

2. If you choose 1, you lose a turn because 1 has no proper factors for your opponent to choose. A composite number with many proper factors would be a bad first move, because your opponent would get many points. Composite numbers with factor sums that are greater than the number are the worst first moves. For example, if you choose 30 or 24 as a first move, your opponent will score 12 points more than you will. Not all composite numbers are bad first moves. For example, if you choose 25, you will get 25 points and your opponent will only get 6.

3. A prime number has only two factors: the number itself and 1. In the Factor Game, prime numbers are good first moves. However, you should choose a prime number only as the *first* move. If you chose a prime for any other move, you would lose a turn, because the only proper factor, 1, would have already been circled.

Mathematical Reflections

In Investigation 1, you played and analyzed the Factor Game. These questions will help you summarize what you have learned:

1 Which numbers are good first moves? What makes these numbers good moves?

2 Which numbers are bad first moves? What makes these numbers bad moves?

3 What did your analysis of the factor game tell you about prime numbers?

Think about your answers to these questions, discuss your ideas with other students and your teacher, and then write a summary of your findings in your journal.

Have you remembered to write about your special number?

Tip for the Linguistically Diverse Classroom

Original Rebus The Original Rebus technique is described in detail in *Getting to Know Connected Mathematics*. Students make their own copy of the text before it is discussed. During discussion, they generate their own rebuses for words they do not understand as the words are made comprehensible through pictures, objects, or demonstrations. Example: Question 1 key words for which students may make rebuses: *numbers* (1, 2, 3, 4, …); *first* (1st); *good move* (thumbs up).

TEACHING THE INVESTIGATION

1.1 • Playing the Factor Game

This problem gives students an opportunity to learn about factors by playing a two-person board game. On each turn, one player chooses a number, and the other player finds the factors of that number. While playing the game, students become familiar with the factors of the numbers from 2 to 30 and review multiplication and division of small whole numbers.

Launch

Discuss the material on the top of page 6 in the student edition and elaborate on what a factor of a number is. Remind students that there are two ways to think of a factor: as one of the numbers that is multiplied to get a product, and as a divisor of a number. You could ask students to give examples:

What factors can you multiply to get a product of 10?

When you feel your students understand what a factor is, introduce the Factor Game. The rules for the game and a sample game are given in the student edition, but the best way to get students started is to play a game against the class using the game board on Transparency 1.1. Rather than reading all the rules at the start, explain the rules as the need arises during the game. When you play against the class, we suggest that you take your turn first and that you choose a *non-prime* number, such as 26, for your first move. This way, students can discover the power of a prime first move.

For the Teacher: A Note on Calculators

In the Connected Mathematics curriculum, we assume that students have access to calculators at all times. However, we hope that students will develop good estimation and mental arithmetic skills. This means that you need to give your students guidelines about the appropriate uses of calculators. In some classes, students may be ready to do all of the arithmetic in the Factor Game without the help of calculators. In other classes, students may need to use calculators to check their mental computations. You need to make a judgement call about whether to use the game as an opportunity for practice in mental arithmetic or to encourage your students to use calculators. After students have a sense of the Factor Game, you may find it appropriate to encourage them to use calculators to keep running totals of their scores.

Explore

Have students play the game two or three times with a partner.

As you play the game, think about the questions I am writing on the board.

Write the following questions on the board:

- Is it better to go first or second? Why?

- What is the best first move? Why?

- How do you know when the game is over?

Summarize

You may want to have a few students share some ideas they discovered while playing the game. However, since Problem 1.2 is an analysis of the game, you can delay an extensive summary until then.

1.2 • Playing to Win the Factor Game

This problem engages students in systematically analyzing the Factor Game. As they were playing the game, certain strategies may have occured to them. Now they are encouraged to verbalize—and possibly explain—their insights.

Launch

The questions you wrote on the board in the Explore section of the last problem help to launch this problem.

> Thinking about the best first move in the Factor Game makes me wonder what the results would be for each number if I chose it as my first move. What if I chose 1 or 2 or 3? How many points would I get? How many points would my opponent get?

> Let's find the results for every possible first move. Can you think of a way that we can organize our work so that we can see patterns and determine which moves are good and which moves are bad?

Give your students a chance to suggest ways to approach the analysis and organization of their work. If no good ideas surface, have them consider the tabular organization presented in the student edition. Once the students and you have agreed on a scheme for organizing the data, remind them of what they are trying to determine. (If you want to provide your students with a chart for recording, use Labsheet 1.2.)

> Remember, you are exploring what your score and your opponent's score would be if you chose each of the numbers from 1 through 30 as your first move. When your chart is complete, write the answers for Problem 1.2 and Problem 1.2 Follow-Up in your journal.

Explore

Give students 5 to 10 minutes to work on their charts individually. Then allow time for them to work with a partner to compare, correct, and complete their charts. You may want to make and display a class chart so you and your students can refer to it during the rest of the unit. A possible chart is given on the next page.

First move	Proper factors	My score	Opponent's score
1	none	lose a turn	0
2	1	2	1
3	1	3	1
4	1, 2	4	3
5	1	5	1
6	1, 2, 3	6	6
7	1	7	1
8	1, 2, 4	8	7
9	1, 3	9	4
10	1, 2, 5	10	8
11	1	11	1
12	1, 2, 3, 4, 6	12	16
13	1	13	1
14	1, 2, 7	14	10
15	1, 3, 5	15	9
16	1, 2, 4, 8	16	15
17	1	17	1
18	1, 2, 3, 6, 9	18	21
19	1	19	1
20	1, 2, 4, 5, 10	20	22
21	1, 3, 7	21	11
22	1, 2, 11	22	14
23	1	23	1
24	1, 2, 3, 4, 6, 8, 12	24	36
25	1, 5	25	6
26	1, 2, 13	26	16
27	1, 3, 9	27	13
28	1, 2, 4, 7, 14	28	28
29	1	29	1
30	1, 2, 3, 5, 6, 10, 15	30	42

For the Teacher: Factor Game First Moves

The chart indicates that prime numbers are good first moves, especially large primes like 29. (Note that prime numbers are only legal when they are first moves. Once a first move has been made, all primes are illegal because their only proper factor, 1, will have already been circled.)

This chart is also a good display of abundant, deficient, and perfect numbers (explained in ACE question 20). The number 24, for example, is abundant because the sum of its proper factors *is more than* 24. The number 16 is deficient because the sum of its proper factors *is less than* 16. The number 6 is perfect because the sum of its proper factors *equals* 6. Note that 6 and 28 are the only perfect numbers between 1 and 30.

Summarize

A good way to summarize is to have students share their answers to Problem 1.2 and Problem 1.2 Follow-Up with the class. Students should record the results of the discussion in their journals, either in class or as a part of their homework.

You may wish to discuss the fact that the number 1 is neither prime nor composite because it has no proper factors at all.

Additional Answers

Answers to Problem 1.2

C. Here are some patterns students have observed:

- María noticed that 1 is a factor of all numbers.
- Kiona noticed that 1 is the worst first move because you lose a turn.
- Jeff noticed that some numbers have only two factors. Some students noticed that the factors are 1 and that number itself.
- Aisha said that all of the numbers with two factors are odd except 2.
- Loren noticed that the numbers 4, 9, 16, and 25 have an odd number of factors. Brianna noticed that these numbers are even, odd, even, odd and predicted that the next one would be even.
- In addition to the patterns students noticed, Mike made the statement that 24 is worse than 30 because you get fewer points with 24.
- Basil replied that 30 is worse than 24 because it is harder to catch up to 42. (Students have a hard time understanding the complexity of 24 versus 30 as a first move. The fact that it is the *difference* between the scores of you and your opponent that matters is a difficult concept to grasp.)

ACE Answers

10a.

Possible first move	Proper factors	My score	Opponent's score
31	1	31	1
32	1, 2, 4, 8, 16	32	31
33	1, 3, 11	33	15
34	1, 2, 17	34	20
35	1, 5, 7	35	13
36	1, 2, 3, 4, 6, 9, 12, 18	36	55
37	1	37	1
38	1, 2, 19	38	22
39	1, 3, 13	39	17
40	1, 2, 4, 5, 8, 10, 20	40	50
41	1	41	1
42	1, 2, 3, 6, 7, 14, 21	42	54
43	1	43	1
44	1, 2, 4, 11, 22	44	40
45	1, 3, 5, 9, 15	45	33
46	1, 2, 23	46	26
47	1	47	1
48	1, 2, 3, 4, 6, 8, 12, 16, 24	48	76
49	1, 7	49	8

21c. Possible answers: 8, 32, or any power of 2; The name *near-perfect* fits because the sum of the factors is one less than the total needed for the number to be perfect.

Your first move	Your opponent's score
2	1
4	1 + 2 = 3
8	1 + 2 + 4 = 7
16	1 + 2 + 4 + 8 = 15
32	1 + 2 + 4 + 8 + 16 = 31

For the Teacher: Finding Near-Perfect Numbers

Near-perfect numbers are useful for finding perfect numbers. Euclid discovered this method:

1. Start with a near-perfect number whose proper factors have a prime sum.

2. Multiply the sum of the factors by the largest power of 2 less than the sum. The product will be a perfect number.

Examples: The number 4 is near-perfect, and the sum of its proper factors is 3, which is prime. The largest power of 2 less than 3 is 2, and $3 \times 2 = 6$, which is perfect. The number 8 is also near-perfect, and the sum of its proper factor is 7, which is prime. The largest power of 2 less than 7 is 4, and $7 \times 4 = 28$, which is perfect. Euclid's method will not work for the near-perfect number 16 because the sum of its proper factors is 15, which is not prime.

Euclid's method always produces even perfect numbers. No one knows whether there are any odd perfect numbers!

The Product Game

In the Factor Game, students start with a number and find its factors. In the Product Game, students start with factors and multiply to find the product. The two games work well together because they help students to see the relationship between products and factors. Students play the Product Game in Problem 2.1. In Problem 2.2, they make their own game boards. The task of creating a new game is challenging to most students. They learn a lot by experimenting and by making mistakes about what factors and products to include in a game. In Problem 2.3, students use Venn diagrams to represent the relationships between the factors or products of two numbers.

Mathematical and Problem-Solving Goals

- **To review multiplication facts**

- **To develop understanding of factors and multiples and of the relationships between them**

- **To understand that some products are the result of more than one factor pair (for example, $18 = 9 \times 2$ and $18 = 6 \times 3$)**

- **To develop strategies for winning the Product Game**

- **To create a new Product Game to play with a friend**

Materials		
Problem	For students	For the teacher
All	Calculators, blank transparency film and transparency markers (optional: for recording results)	Transparencies 2.1 to 2.3 (optional)
2.1	Labsheet 2.1 (1 per pair), paper clips (2 per pair); colored chips (about 12 each of 2 colors per pair), or colored pens, pencils, or markers	
2.2	Materials for constructing game boards (e.g., grid paper, construction paper, cardboard, markers), paper clips, colored chips	

INVESTIGATION 2

The Product Game

In the Factor Game, you start with a number and find its factors. In the Product Game, you start with factors and find their product. The diagram shows the relationship between factors and their product.

2.1 Playing the Product Game

The Product Game board consists of a list of factors and a grid of products. Two players compete to get four squares in a row—up and down, across, or diagonally. To play the Product Game, you will need Labsheet 2.1, two paper clips, and colored markers or game chips. The rules for the Product Game are given on the next page.

The Product Game

1	2	3	4	5	6
7	8	9	10	12	14
15	16	18	20	21	24
25	27	28	30	32	35
36	40	42	45	**48**	49
54	56	63	64	72	81

Factors:

1   2   3   4   5   6   7   8   9

At a Glance

Grouping:
Pairs

Launch

- Review the definition of product.

- Introduce the Product Game by playing a game against your class.

Explore

- Have students play the Product Game two or three times with a partner.

- As students play the game, ask them to think about whether it is better to go first or second and to record strategies that they discover.

Summarize

- Hold a class discussion in which students share strategies they have found.

Assignment Choices

ACE questions 1–8, 13, 17–20, and unassigned choices from earlier problems

Problem 2.1

Play the Product Game several times with a partner. Look for interesting patterns and winning strategies. Make notes of your observations.

Product Game Rules

1. Player A puts a paper clip on a number in the factor list. Player A does not mark a square on the product grid because only one factor has been marked; it takes two factors to make a product.
2. Player B puts the other paper clip on any number in the factor list (including the same number marked by Player A) and then shades or covers the product of the two factors on the product grid.
3. Player A moves *either one* of the paper clips to another number and then shades or covers the new product.
4. Each player, in turn, moves a paper clip and marks a product. If a product is already marked, the player does not get a mark for that turn. The winner is the first player to mark four squares in a row—up and down, across, or diagonally.

▓ Problem 2.1 Follow-Up

1. Suppose one of the paper clips is on 5. What products can you make by moving the other paper clip?

The products you listed in question 1 are multiples of 5. A **multiple** of a number is the product of that number and another whole number.

If a number is a multiple of 5, then 5 is a factor of that number. These four sentences are all ways of expressing $5 \times 3 = 15$:

5 is a factor of 15.
3 is a factor of 15.
15 is a multiple of 5.
15 is a multiple of 3.

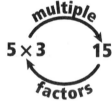

2. List five multiples of 5 that are not on the game board.
3. Suppose one of the paper clips is on 3. What products can you make by moving the other paper clip?
4. List five multiples of 3 that are not on the game board.

Answers to Problem 2.1 Follow-Up

1. $5 \times 1 = 5$, $5 \times 2 = 10$, $5 \times 3 = 15$, $5 \times 4 = 20$, $5 \times 5 = 25$, $5 \times 6 = 30$, $5 \times 7 = 35$, $5 \times 8 = 40$, and $5 \times 9 = 45$

2. Possible answer: 50, 55, 60, 65, and 70

3. 3, 6, 9, 12, 15, 18, 21, 24, and 27

4. Possible answer: 33, 39, 51, 57, and 60

2.2 **Making Your Own Product Game**

Suppose you want to create a product game that takes less time to play or, perhaps, more time to play than the game with the 6 × 6 product grid. You would have to decide what numbers to include in the factor list and what products to include in the product grid.

Problem 2.2

Work with your partner to design a new game board for the Product Game.
- Choose factors to include in your factor list.
- Determine the products you need to include on the game board.
- Find a game board that will accommodate all the products.
- Decide how many squares a player must get in a row—up and down, across, or diagonally—to win.

Make the game board. Play your game against your partner; then make any changes you both agree would make your game better.

Switch game boards with another pair, and play their game. Give them some written suggestions about how they can improve their game. Read the suggestions for improving your game, then make any changes you and your partner think are necessary.

▓ Problem 2.2 Follow-Up

Write a paragraph about why you think your game board is interesting to use for playing the Product Game. In the paragraph, describe any problems you ran into while making the board, and explain how you solved them.

Answer to Problem 2.2

The game boards that students create will vary. See the Assessment Resources section for samples of student game boards and a possible scoring rubric.

Answer to Problem 2.2 Follow-Up

Answers will vary.

▪ ▪ ▪ ▪ ▪ ▪ ▪ ▪
At a Glance

Grouping:
Pairs

Launch

■ Review strategies for playing the Product Game.

■ Help students to see that a good Product Game board has a product for every pair of factors in the factor list.

■ Read the problem with the class, and make sure they understand the instructions.

Explore

■ Circulate as pairs make their Product Game boards.

■ If a group is having difficulty, help them find the correct list of products.

Summarize

■ Give students a chance to share their games with the class and to explain how they improved them based on feedback from their classmates.

Assignment Choices

ACE questions 9, 10, 14, and unassigned choices from earlier problems

Classifying Numbers

**Grouping:
Pairs**

Launch

- Draw a Venn diagram with a circle for the factors of 30 and a circle for the factors of 36.

- Work with students to place the numbers from 1 to 12 in the correct regions of the diagram.

Explore

- Have students work in pairs on Problem 2.3 and Problem 2.3 Follow-Up.

Summarize

- Choose pairs of students to present and explain their solutions to the class.

Assignment Choices

ACE questions 11, 12, 15, 16, and unassigned choices from earlier problems

---

2.3 Classifying Numbers

Now that you know how to find the factors and multiples of a number, you can explore how the factors and multiples of two or more numbers are related. Venn diagrams are useful tools for exploring these relationships. A **Venn diagram** uses circles to show things that belong together. For example, the Venn diagram below shows one way to group whole numbers.

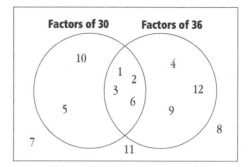

One circle represents all the whole numbers that are factors of 30. The other circle represents all the whole numbers that are factors of 36. The first 12 whole numbers have been placed in the correct regions of the diagram. Notice that the numbers that are not factors of 30 or 36 lie outside the circles. Why do the circles intersect (overlap)? What do the numbers in the intersection have in common?

Problem 2.3

Copy the Venn diagram below.

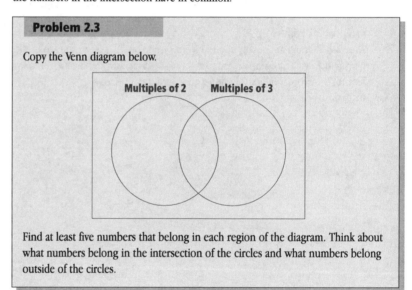

Find at least five numbers that belong in each region of the diagram. Think about what numbers belong in the intersection of the circles and what numbers belong outside of the circles.

Answer to Problem 2.3

Possible answer:

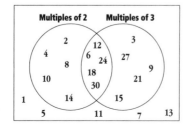

Problem 2.3 Follow-Up

1. What factors do the numbers in the intersection of the circles have in common?
2. Add a new circle to the diagram with the label "Multiples of 5," as shown below. Replace your numbers in the correct regions, and make sure you have at least two numbers in each part of the diagram.

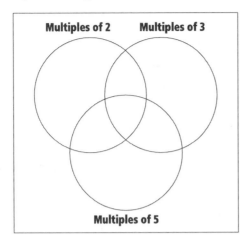

Answers to Problem 2.3 Follow-Up

1. 1, 2, 3, and 6

2. Possible answer:

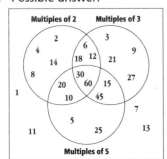

Note that the numbers in the intersection of all three circles are multiples of 30.

Answers

Applications

1. 2 and 9, 3 and 6

2. Possible answer: 16 and 36; 16 = 4 × 4 and 16 = 2 × 8; 36 = 12 × 3, 36 = 9 × 4 and 36 = 6 × 6. Also, 12 and 24 are possible answers.

3. 1, 3, and 9

4a. You can move the paper clip from the 6 to make the products 5 × 1, 5 × 2, 5 × 3, 5 × 4, 5 × 5, 5 × 7, 5 × 8, and 5 × 9. You can move the paper clip from the 5 to make the products 6 × 1, 6 × 2, 6 × 3, 6 × 4, 6 × 6, 6 × 7, 6 × 8, and 6 × 9. The products 6 × 3 and 6 × 5 are already taken.

4b. 5 × 3, 5 × 4, 5 × 9, and 6 × 7

4c. 6 × 7

4d. Possible answer: 6 × 7; It allows you to block your opponent.

5. Possible answers: 2 × 42, 3 × 28, 4 × 21, 6 × 14, 7 × 12

6. 5 × 29

7. Possible answers: 2 × 125, 5 × 50, 10 × 25

8. Possible answers: 2 × 150, 3 × 100, 4 × 75, 5 × 60, 6 × 50, 10 × 30,

---

Applications • Connections • Extensions

As you work on these ACE questions, use your calculator whenever you need it.

Applications

1. Marena just marked 18 on the 6 × 6 Product Game board. On which factors might the paper clips be? List all the possibilities.

2. Find two products on the board, other than 18, that can be made in more than one way. List all the factor pairs that give each product.

3. On the 6 × 6 Product Game board, 81 is a multiple of which factors?

4. On the 6 × 6 Product Game board, suppose your markers are on 16, 18, and 28, and your opponent's markers are on 14, 21, and 30. The paper clips are on 5 and 6. It is your turn to move a paper clip.

a. List the possible moves you could make.

b. Which move(s) would give you three markers in a row?

c. Which move(s) would allow you to block your opponent?

d. Which move would you make? Explain your strategy.

The Product Game

1	2	3	4	5	6
7	8	9	10	12	14
15	16	18	20	21	24
25	27	28	30	32	35
36	40	42	45	48	49
54	56	63	64	72	81

Factors:
1 2 3 4 5 6 7 8 9

In 5–8, find two numbers that can be multiplied to give each product. Do not use 1 as one of the numbers.

5. 84 **6.** 145 **7.** 250 **8.** 300

9. What factors were used to create this Product Game board?

4	6	14
9	21	49

Factors: ___ ___ ___

10. What factors were used to create this Product Game board? What number is missing from the grid?

9	15	18	■
21	?	30	35
■	36	42	49

Factors: ___ ___ ___ ___

11. Draw and label a Venn diagram in which one circle represents multiples of 3 and another circle represents multiples of 5. Place the multiples of 3 and the multiples of 5 from 1 to 60 in the appropriate regions of the diagram. The numbers that are multiples of both 3 and 5 are the **common multiples** of 3 and 5. These numbers go in the intersection of the two circles.

12. Find at least five numbers that belong in each of the regions of this Venn diagram.

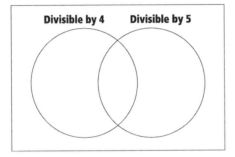

Divisible by 4   Divisible by 5

Connections

13. What numbers is 36 a multiple of?

14. Using the words *factor, divisor, multiple, product,* and *divisible by*, write as many statements as you can about the mathematical sentence $7 \times 9 = 63$.

9. 2, 3, and 7
10. 3, 5, 6, and 7; 25
11. See below left.
12. See below left.

Connections

13. 1, 2, 3, 4, 6, 9, 12, 18, and 36

14. Possible answers: 7 and 9 are factors of 63. 63 is the product of 7 and 9. 7 and 9 are divisors of 63. 63 is a multiple of 7. 63 is a multiple of 9. 63 is divisible by 7. 63 is divisible by 9.

11.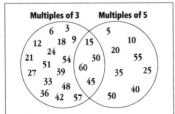

12. Possible answer:

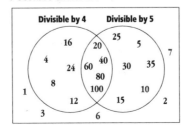

15. See below right.

16. 44 and 88

17. 1, 2, 4, 5, 10, or 20; Each of these numbers divides both 20 and 40 evenly.

18. 24 shifts of 1 hour, 12 shifts of 2 hours, 8 shifts of 3 hours, 6 shifts of 4 hours, 4 shifts of 6 hours, 3 shifts of 8 hours, 2 shifts of 12 hours, or 1 shift of 24 hours

19a. Since 60 has many factors, it can be divided several ways into equal parts. Because 59 and 61 are prime, they cannot be divided into parts.

19b. Possible answers: 48, 64, 72, or 80; These numbers have many factors and can be subdivided easily.

Extensions

20. The numbers that have two even digits (Clue 2) and give a remainder of 4 when divided by 5 (Clue 1) are 24, 44, 64, and 84. Of these numbers, 64 is the only one with digits that add to 10 (Clue 3). The number is 64.

---

15. Draw and label a Venn diagram in which one circle contains the **divisors** (factors) of 42 and the other contains the divisors of 60. The divisors of both 42 and 60 are the **common factors** of the two numbers. The common factors should go in the intersection of the two circles.

16. Find all the common multiples of 4 and 11 that are less than 100.

17. The cast of the school play had a party at the drama teacher's house. There were 20 cookies and 40 carrot sticks served as refreshments. Each cast member had the same number of whole cookies and the same number of whole carrot sticks, and nothing was left over. The drama teacher did not eat. How many cast members might have been at the party? Explain your answer.

18. A restaurant is open 24 hours a day. The manager wants to divide the day into workshifts of equal length. Show the different ways this can be done. The shifts should not overlap, and all shifts should be a whole number of hours long.

19 a. In developing ways to calculate time, astronomers divided an hour into 60 minutes. Why is 60 a good choice (better than 59 or 61)?

b. If you were to select another number to represent the minutes in an hour, what would be a good choice? Why?

Extensions

20. What is my number?
Clue 1 When you divide my number by 5, the remainder is 4.
Clue 2 My number has two digits, and both digits are even.
Clue 3 The sum of the digits is 10.

15.

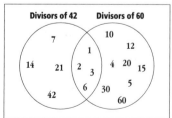

Mathematical Reflections

In this investigation, you played and analyzed the Product Game. These questions will help you summarize what you have learned:

1 In the Product Game, describe the relationship between the numbers in the factor list and the products in the grid.

2 What are the multiples of a number and how do you find them?

3 Using the words *factor, divisor, multiple,* and *divisible by,* write as many statements as you can about this mathematical sentence:

$$4 \times 7 = 28$$

Think about your answers to these questions, discuss your ideas with other students and your teacher, and then write a summary of your findings in your journal.

Write something new that you have learned about your special number now that you have played the Factor Game and the Product Game. Would your special number be a good first move in either game? Why or why not?

Possible Answers

1. The numbers in the grid are all the products that can be obtained by multiplying two numbers in the factor list (including products of each number and itself).

2. The multiples of a number are products of the number and other whole numbers. A multiple of a number has the number as a factor. You find the multiples of a number by multiplying the number by each whole number, beginning with 1. The multiples of a number are the number times 1, the number times 2, the number times 3, and so on.

3. Possible answers: 4 is a factor of 28; 7 is a factor of 28; 4 is a divisor of 28; 7 is a divisor of 28; 28 is a multiple of 4; 28 is a multiple of 7; 28 is divisible by 7; 28 is divisible by 4.

TEACHING THE INVESTIGATION

2.1 • Playing the Product Game

The Factor Game required students to find factors of numbers. In the Product Game, students explore multiples.

Launch

Before you introduce the game, make sure your students understand what a product is.

> We are going to learn to play a new game called the Product Game. What does the word *product* mean?

When you are satisfied students can give examples of products with understanding, introduce the Product Game. You may want to have students read pages 17 and 18 in the student edition. These pages give a quick overview of the game.

The best way to explain the rules is to play a game against the class. Use Transparency 2.1 on the overhead projector, or draw a game board on the chalkboard.

The Product Game

1	2	3	4	5	6
7	8	9	10	12	14
15	16	18	20	21	24
25	27	28	30	32	35
36	40	42	45	48	49
54	56	63	64	72	81

Factors:
 1 2 3 4 5 6 7 8 9

Explain that the list of numbers at the bottom of the board are factors and that the numbers in the grid are the products that can be made by multiplying any two factors. When you play the game, use two colors to mark the products—one to mark the class's products and the other to mark your own.

A typical game might begin like this:

- Place a paper clip on 4 in the factor list. Explain to the class that you do not get to mark a product in the grid, because it takes two factors to make a product.

- Ask the class to select a factor. Suppose they pick 7. Place a paper clip on 7. Ask the class to compute the product of 4 and 7. Mark the result, 28, on the game board using the class's color. **Note:** There is no need to keep score, because the goal of the game is to place four markers in a row—up and down, across, or diagonally.

- Remove the paper clip from 7 and place it on the 4 in the factor list. Explain to the class that since the factors are both 4, the product is 16. Use your color to mark 16 on the product grid.

- Continue playing until you or your class get four in a row.

Explore

Have students pair up to play the game.

> As you play the game, think about whether it is better to go first or second. Make notes about the strategies that will help you win the game.

After students have played the game two or three times, have them work on Problem 2.1 Follow-Up. These questions will prepare them for the class summary.

Summarize

Have a class discussion about whether it is better to go first or second. Have students share any strategies they discovered while playing the game. Here are some comments students have made:

- Diaco said it is better to go second, because if you go first, you do not get to make a move on the board.

- Betty said that when you get toward the end of the game, you have to avoid the factors of the numbers your opponent needs.

- Jabé said that if you had to go first, you should choose the number 1 because it gives your opponent fewer choices about where to go to get four in a row.

Go over Problem 2.1 Follow-Up with your class. This is especially important, since the word *multiple* is introduced for the first time.

2.2 • Making Your Own Product Game

In this problem, students make their own product games. As students determine what products and factors to include on their gameboards, they practice and review multiplication and division facts.

Launch

Spend some time reviewing students' strategies for playing the Product Game.

> We have been playing the Product Game and discussing strategies you can use to win. Look back at the board. Does it contain all the products you can make from the list of factors?

> What products would we need to add if we added 10 to the factor list?

Multiplying 10 by the other factors on the list gives the products 10, 20, 30, 40, 50, 60, 70, 80, 90, and 100. Help students to see that 10, 20, 30, and 40 are already on the board. (You might ask why.) Therefore, you would need to add only 50, 60, 70, 80, 90, and 100. You want students to see that every product, including the squares of the factors, must be on the game board to make a good game. Sometimes students have to experience frustration while making their game boards before they realize that every product must be included.

When you feel your students are ready, have them read the problem. Make sure students understand the instructions before they start working on their game boards.

For the Teacher: Extending the Product Game

To create a new game, students might first decide what factors they want to use and then determine which products are possible. If, for example, students choose the factors 1, 2, 3, and 4, the products would be 1, 2, 3, 4, 6, 8, 9, 12, and 16. This would create a nice 3 × 3 game board. The rules could be modified so that three in a row would win.

Students need to use enough factors to make their game interesting. For example, the factors 1, 2, and 3 give the products 1, 2, 3, 4, 6, and 9. A 3 × 2 grid would accommodate these six products, but this would not make a very interesting game. Only two markers in a row would be required to win, so the game would end on the second turn of the first player!

Instead of choosing the factors first, students can select the size of the product grid they want, then work backward to find the factors needed to fill the board. Interested students might be challenged to find the factors needed to create a 10 × 10 board (the factors 1 through 16 are needed, and there will be three blank spaces). You might want to help students organize their work as in the table below.

Factor	Products of the factor and numbers less than or equal to the factor	Number of products added to the list*	Total number of products on the list
1	1	1	1
2	2, 4	2	3
3	3, 6, 9	3	6
4	4, 8, 12, 16	3	9
5	5, 10, 15, 20, 25	5	14
6	6, 12, 18, 24, 30, 36	4	18
7	7, 14, 21, 28, 35, 42, 49	7	25
8	8, 16, 24, 32, 40, 48, 56, 64	5	30
9	9, 18, 27, 36, 45, 54, 63, 72, 81	6	36
10	10, 20, 30, 40, 50, 60, 70, 80, 90, 100	6	42
11	11, 22, 33, 44, 55, 66, 77, 88, 99, 110, 121	11	53
12	12, 24, 36, 48, 60, 72, 84, 96, 108, 120, 132, 144	6	59
13	13, 26, 39, 52, 65, 78, 91, 104, 117, 130, 143, 156, 169	13	72
14	14, 28, 42, 56, 70, 84, 98, 112, 126, 140, 154, 168, 182, 196	8	80
15	15, 30, 45, 60, 75, 90, 105, 120, 135, 150, 165 180, 195, 210, 225	9	89
16	16, 32, 48, 64, 80, 96, 112, 128, 144, 160, 176 192, 208, 224, 240, 256	8	97

*Products in italics have already been used; they are not counted again.

Explore

If a group is having difficulty, check over their list of products and help them get the products correct.

I notice that the product of 4 and 5 is not on your list. Have you checked to make sure you have all of the products?

Ask questions that will help students focus on the relationship between the list of products and the size of the game board. Some boards will need to have to have blanks or free spaces.

What size game board will hold all of your products? Is this the smallest board you can use?

Circulate while students are making their games, and help keep the groups focused on the task. When students are playing each other's games, remind them that it is very important that they give good feedback.

As you are playing your own or another group's game, if you think it is interesting and should be shared with the rest of the class, let me know.

When students have finished making their boards ask them to work on the summary paragraph described in Problem 2.3 Follow-Up.

Summarize

You can summarize this activity with each group individually. As you interact with a group, observe the problems they are having, and work to help them overcome these problems. Ask the group to explain the steps they went through to create the board. Ask what problems they had and how they solved these problems. Ask how they knew when they had all of the possible products and whether they needed to change the rules to play on their board.

You also could summarize by having groups share their reports with the class. Use the reports to help students focus on characteristics of interesting game boards and the strategies that were used to create them.

Samples of game boards and teacher comments can be found in the Assessment Resources section.

For the Teacher: Sharing Product Games

Display and duplicate games the students find interesting so other students can play them during down time.

2.3 • Classifying Numbers

This problem uses Venn diagrams to organize information about numbers. A Venn diagram uses circles to show sets of numbers or other objects with the same attributes. Your students may have used string circles in the elementary grades to look at relationships or attributes. The important thing in this problem is for students to look for relationships and characteristics of numbers and to determine what numbers belong to a descriptor and what numbers belong to more than one descriptor.

Launch

You might start the lesson by drawing two overlapping circles, labeled "Factors of 30" and "Factors of 36," on the board.

> Give me some examples of numbers that go in each circle.

Record a few numbers that students give, always asking in which area of the diagram the number goes.

> Are there any numbers that belong in both circles? Why or why not?

Here you are hoping that students will see that there are numbers that are factors of both 30 and 36.

> We put the numbers that belong in both circles in the intersection, or overlap, of the circles.

Write some numbers that are factors of both 30 and 36, for example 2 and 6, in the intersection of the circles.

> Are there any numbers that do not belong in either circle?

Help students see that 7, 8, 11, and many other numbers are not factors of 30 or 36, and therefore do not belong in either circle. Draw a rectangle that encloses the circles.

> We can show these numbers by putting them in the area ouside of the circles.

Write these numbers inside the rectangle and outside of the circles.

Explore

Students should work in pairs on Problem 2.3 and Problem 2.3 Follow-Up.

Summarize

One way to summarize is to have each group draw their Venn diagram on a blank transparency. The groups can then present their work at the overhead and explain their thinking. Or, select three pairs of students to put their work on the board. Have one pair draw their Venn diagram for Problem 2.3 and the other two pairs give their answers to Problem 2.3 Follow-Up.

> If any group wants to add or disagree with anything on the board, come up and write your comments in another color.

In the discussion, have students share the strategies that they used to solve the problems. Be sure to ask what is special about the numbers in the intersection of the circles. Students should realize that these numbers are divisible by both 2 and 3, which means they are also divisible by 6. In other words, they are all multiples of 6.

Factor Pairs

In Problem 3.1, Arranging Space, students use square tiles to build all possible rectangles with areas of 12 square units and 16 square units. In Problem 3.2, Finding Patterns, students make rectangles for each number from 1 to 30. Displaying the rectangles will help students to visualize a factor pair as the dimensions of a rectangle whose area is the given number. The displays will also help students describe prime and square numbers. The work in this investigation provides a foundation for discussing how many numbers must be checked to ensure that all factors of a number have been found. In Problem 3.3, Reasoning with Odd and Even Numbers, students make and prove conjectures about sums and products of even and odd numbers.

Mathematical and Problem-Solving Goals

- **To recognize that factors come in pairs**

- **To visualize and represent a factor pair as the dimensions of a rectangle with the given number as its area**

- **To determine whether a number is prime or composite, even or odd, and square or nonsquare based on its factor pairs**

- **To develop an informal sense of how many factors must be checked to be sure all the factors of a number have been found**

Materials		
Problem	**For students**	**For the teacher**
All	Calculators	Transparencies 3.1 to 3.3 (optional)
3.1	Square tiles (about 30 per pair); grid paper (provided as a blackline master)	
3.2	Grid paper, blank sheets of paper, scissors, tape, square tiles (optional; about 30 per pair)	
3.3	Grid paper (optional), square tiles (optional; about 30 per pair)	

Student Pages 26–35   Teaching the Investigation 35a–35f

Arranging Space

At a Glance

Grouping:
Pairs

Launch

- Tell the story of the art exhibit from the student edition.

Explore

- Have students work in pairs on the problem.

Summarize

- As a class, discuss the solutions to the problem.

Factor Pairs

In the Factor Game and the Product Game, you found that factors come in pairs. Once you know one factor of a number, you can find another factor. For example, 3 is a factor of 12, and because $3 \times 4 = 12$, you know 4 is also a factor of 12. In this investigation, you will look at factor pairs in a different way.

3.1 Arranging Space

Every year, Meridian Park has an exhibit of arts and crafts. People who want to exhibit their work rent a space for $20 per square yard. All exhibit spaces must have a rectangular shape. The length and width of an exhibit space must be whole numbers of yards.

Problem 3.1

Terrapin Crafts wants to rent a space of 12 square yards.

A. Use 12 square tiles to represent the 12 square yards. Find all the possible ways the Terrapin Crafts owner can arrange the squares. Copy each rectangle you make onto grid paper, and label it with its dimensions (length and width).

B. How are the rectangles you found and the factors of 12 related?

Suppose Terrapin Crafts decided it wanted a space of 16 square yards.

C. Find all the possible ways the Terrapin Crafts owner can arrange the 16 square yards. Copy each rectangle you make onto grid paper, and label it with its dimensions.

D. How are these rectangles and the factors of 16 related?

Assignment Choices

ACE question 16 and unassigned choices from earlier problems

Answers to Problem 3.1

A. See page 35d.

B. The factors of 12 are the dimensions of the rectangles.

C. The rectangles for 16 have dimensions 1×16, 2×8, 4×4, 8×2, and 16×1.

D. The factors of 16 are the dimensions of the rectangles.

Answer to Problem 3.1 Follow-Up

1, 2, and 4

■ **Problem 3.1 Follow-Up**

What factors do 12 and 16 have in common?

3.2 Finding Patterns

Will likes to find number patterns. He wonders if there are any interesting patterns in the rectangles that can be made for the numbers from 1 to 30.

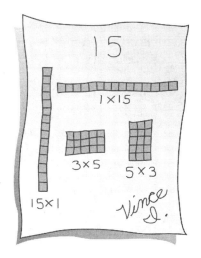

In this problem, your class will make rectangles for all the whole numbers from 1 through 30. When all the rectangles are displayed, you can look for interesting patterns.

Work with a partner or a small group so that you can check each other's work. With your teacher, decide which numbers your group will be responsible for.

Problem 3.2

Work with your group to decide how to divide up the work for the numbers you have been assigned.

Cut out a grid-paper model of each rectangle you can make for each of the numbers you have been assigned. You may want to use tiles to help you find the rectangles.

Write each number at the top of a sheet of paper, and tape all the rectangles for that number to the sheet. Display the sheets of rectangles in order from 1 to 30 around the room.

When all the numbers are displayed, look for patterns. Be prepared to discuss patterns you find with your classmates.

At a Glance

Grouping: Small Groups

Launch

■ Distribute the whole numbers from 1 to 30 among the groups of students.

■ Ask the groups to divide the work so that each member has about the same amount of work to do.

Explore

■ Allow students to work alone to make their rectangles and then to work with their groups to correct their displays.

■ Ask students to look for patterns in the rectangles their group is making.

■ Post the displays.

Summarize

■ Hold a class discussion about the patterns that students have found.

■ Be sure to discuss displays for prime and square numbers.

Answers to Problem 3.2 Follow-Up

1. 24 and 30; Possible answers: composite and abundant

2. 1 has only one rectangle, and 2, 3, 5, 7, 11, 13, 17, 19, 23, and 29 each have two. Possible answer: Except for 1, all these numbers are prime and deficient.

3. 1, 4, 9, 16, and 25

4. The dimensions of the rectangles are the factors of the number. For example, with 12 tiles, you can make rectangles with dimensions 1×12, 2×6, 3×4, 4×3, 6×2, and 12×1. The factors of 12 are the dimensions of these rectangles: 1, 2, 3, 4, 6, and 12.

Assignment Choices

ACE questions 1–8, 17–19, 21–25, and unassigned choices from earlier problems

Reasoning with Odd and Even Numbers

Launch

- Review the concepts of odd number and even number.

- Discuss Jocelyn's tile models for even and odd numbers.

- Discuss what it means to make a conjecture.

Explore

- Have students work in pairs on the problem.

Summarize

- Hold a class discussion in which students present and explain their solutions.

Assignment Choices

ACE questions 10–15, and unassigned choices from earlier problems (Assign 26–30 as an extra challenge.)

Assessment

It is appropriate to use Quiz A and Check-Up 1 after this problem.

■ **Problem 3.2 Follow-Up**

1. Which numbers have the most rectangles? What kind of numbers are these?

2. Which numbers have the fewest rectangles? What kind of numbers are these?

3. Which numbers are **square numbers** (numbers whose tiles can be arranged to form a square)?

4. If you know the rectangles you can make for a number, how can you use this information to list the factors of the number? Use an example to show your thinking.

3.3 **Reasoning with Odd and Even Numbers**

An **even number** is a number that has 2 as a factor. An **odd number** is a number that does not have 2 as a factor. In this problem, you will study patterns involving odd and even numbers. First, you will learn a way of modeling odd and even numbers. Then, you will make conjectures about sums and products of odd and even numbers. A *conjecture* is your best guess about a relationship. You can use the models to justify, or prove, your conjectures.

" AN ODD NUMBER "

Will's friend, Jocelyn, makes models for whole numbers by arranging square tiles in a special pattern. Here are Jocelyn's tile models for the numbers from 1 to 7.

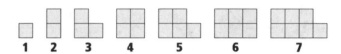

Discuss with your class how the models of even numbers are different from the models of odd numbers. Then describe the models for 50 and 99.

Problem 3.3

Make a conjecture about whether each result below will be even or odd. Then use tile models or some other method to justify your conjecture.

A. The sum of two even numbers

B. The sum of two odd numbers

C. The sum of an odd number and an even number

D. The product of two even numbers

E. The product of two odd numbers

F. The product of an odd number and an even number

▓ Problem 3.3 Follow-Up

1. Is 0 an even number or an odd number? Explain your answer.

2. Without building a tile model, how can you tell whether a sum of numbers—such as 127 + 38—is even or odd?

Answers to Problem 3.3

See page 35e.

Answers to Problem 3.3 Follow-Up

1. even; Possible explanations: 0 divided by 2 gives a remainder of 0. The whole numbers are distributed on the number line so that every other number is odd and every other number is even. Since 1 is odd, 0 must be even.

2. You can use the conjectures that we proved in the problem. For example, 127 is odd and 38 is even. In the problem, we showed that the sum of an odd number and an even number is odd. So, 127 + 38 is odd.

Answers

Applications

1. 1 × 24, 2 × 12, 3 × 8, 4 × 6, 6 × 4, 8 × 3, 12 × 2, and 24 × 1; 1 and 24, 2 and 12, 3 and 8, 4 and 6

2. 1 × 32, 2 × 16, 4 × 8, 8 × 4, 16 × 2, and 32 × 1; 1 and 32, 2 and 16, 4 and 8

3. 1 × 48, 2 × 24, 3 × 16, 4 × 12, 6 × 8, 8 × 6, 12 × 4, 16 × 3, 24 × 2, and 48 × 1; 1 and 48, 2 and 24, 3 and 16, 4 and 12, 6 and 8

4. 1 × 45, 3 × 15, 5 × 9, 9 × 5, 15 × 3, and 45 × 1; 1 and 45, 3 and 15, 5 and 9

5. 1 × 60, 2 × 30, 3 × 20, 4 × 15, 5 × 12, 6 × 10, 10 × 6, 12 × 5, 15 × 4, 20 × 3, 2 × 30, and 60 × 1; 1 and 60, 2 and 30, 4 and 15, 5 and 12, 6 and 10

6. 1 × 72, 2 × 36, 3 × 24, 4 × 18, 6 × 12, 8 × 9, 9 × 8, 12 × 6, 18 × 4, 24 × 3, 36 × 2, and 72 × 1; 1 and 72, 2 and 36, 3 and 24, 4 and 18, 6 and 12, 8 and 9

7. Every number has itself and 1 as factors. A number with exactly two factors has only itself and 1 as factors. Such a number is *prime*. For example, 31 is a prime number because its only factors are 1 and 31.

8. Factors come in pairs, so a number with an odd number of factors must have a factor pair that is made up of the same number repeated. This means one of the rectangles for the number is a square. We call such a number a square number. Examples are 4, which has 3 factors (1, 2, and 4), and 16, which

---

As you work on these ACE questions, use your calculator whenever you need it.

Applications

In 1–6, give the dimensions of each rectangle that can be made from the given number of tiles. Then, use the dimensions of the rectangles to list all the factor pairs for each number.

1. 24   **2.** 32   **3.** 48

4. 45   **5.** 60   **6.** 72

In 7 and 8, write a description, with examples, of numbers that have the given factors.

7. exactly two factors   **8.** an odd number of factors

9. Lupe has chosen a mystery number. His number is larger than 12 and smaller than 40, and it has exactly three factors. What could his number be? Use the displays of rectangles for the numbers 1 to 30 to help you find Lupe's mystery number. You may need to think about what the displays for the numbers 31 to 40 would look like.

10. Without building a tile model, how can you tell whether a sum of numbers—such as 13 + 45 + 24 + 17 is even or odd?

In 11–14, make a conjecture about whether each result will be odd or even. Use tiles, a picture, or some other way to justify your conjectures.

11. An even number minus an even number

12. An odd number minus an odd number

13. An even number minus an odd number

14. An odd number minus an even number

15. How can you tell whether a number is even or odd? Explain or illustrate your answer in at least two ways.

Connections

16. **a.** List all the numbers less than or equal to 50 that are divisible by 5.

    b. Describe a pattern you see in your list that you can use to determine whether a large number—such as 1,276,549—is divisible by 5.

    c. Which numbers in your list are divisible by 2?

    d. Which numbers in your list are divisible by 10?

    e. How do the lists in parts c and d compare? Why does this result make sense?

17. A group of students designs card displays for football games. They use 100 square cards for each display. Each card contains part of a picture or message. At the game, 100 volunteers hold up the cards to form a complete picture. The students have found that the pictures are most effective if the volunteers sit in a rectangular arrangement. What seating arrangements are possible? Which would you choose? Why?

18. The school band has 64 members. The band marches in the form of a rectangle. What rectangles can the band director make by arranging the members of the band? Which of these arrangements is most appealing to you? Why?

19. How many rectangles can you build with a prime number of square tiles?

has five factors (1, 2, 4, 8, and 16).

9. Since Lupe's number has three factors, it must be a square. The square numbers between 12 and 40 are 16, 25, and 36. Of these numbers, only 25 has exactly three factors. Lupe's mystery number is 25.

10. Possible answer: You can use the conjectures that were proved in Problem 3.3. Since 13 and 45 are both odd, 13 + 45 is even. Since 24 is even and 17 is odd, 24 + 17 is odd. So, 13 + 45 + 24 + 17 is an even plus an odd, which is odd.

11. even; Possible justification: If you start with the rectangle model for an even number and take away a rectangle, you are left with another rectangle.

12. even; Possible justification: If you start with a rectangle with an extra tile and take away a rectangle with an extra tile, you are left with a rectangle.

13. odd; Possible justification: If you start with a rectangle and take away a rectangle with an extra tile, you are left with a rectangle with an extra tile.

14. odd; Possible justification: If you start with a rectangle with an extra tile and take away a rectangle, you are left with a rectangle with an extra tile.

15. Possible answers: If a number has a rectangle with a dimension of 2, the number is even; otherwise, the number is odd. Even numbers end in 0, 2, 4, 6,

or 8; odd numbers end in 1, 3, 5, 7, or 9. Dividing an even number by 2 gives a remainder of 0; dividing an odd number by 2 gives a remainder of 1.

Connections

16a. 0, 5, 10, 15, 20, 25, 30, 35, 40, 45, and 50

16b. Numbers that are divisible by 5 end in 5 or 0, so 1,276,549 is not divisible by 5.

16c. 0, 10, 20, 30, 40, and 50

16d. 0, 10, 20, 30, 40, and 50

16e. The lists are the same; If a number is divisible by both 2 and 5, it is also divisible by their least common multiple, 10.

17. 100 fans in 1 row, 50 fans in 2 rows, 25 fans in 4 rows, 20 fans in 5 rows, 10 fans in 10 rows, 5 fans in 20 rows, 4 fans in 25 rows, 2 fans in 50 rows, or 1 fan in 100 rows; Answers will vary.

18. 1×64, 2×32, 4×16, 8×8, 16×4, 32×2, and 64×1; Answers will vary.

19. 2

Extensions

20. Possible answer: 3, 5, and 20

21. 196 is a square number because $196 = 14 \times 14$.

22. 225 is a square number because $225 = 15 \times 15$.

23. 360 is not a square number because no whole number times itself equals 360.

Extensions

20. Find three numbers you can multiply to get 300.

In 21–23, tell whether each number is a square number. Justify your answer.

21. 196   **22.** 225   **23.** 360

24. a. Find at least five numbers that belong in each region of the Venn diagram below.

b. What do the numbers in the intersection have in common?

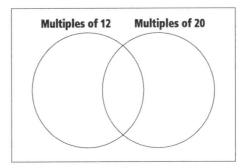

25. a. Below is the complete list of the proper factors of a certain number. What is the number?

1, 2, 3, 4, 6, 7, 12, 14, 21, 28, 42, 49, 84, 98, 147, 196, 294

b. List each of the factor pairs for the number.

c. What rectangles could be made to show the number?

26. For any three consecutive numbers (whole numbers in a row), such as 31, 32, 33, or 52, 53, 54, what is true about odds and evens? Explain your thinking.

27. Ji Young conjectured that, in every three consecutive whole numbers, one number will be divisible by 3. Do you think Ji Young is correct? Explain.

24a. Possible answer:

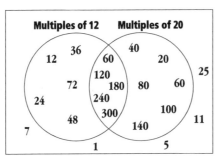

28. How many consecutive numbers do you need to guarantee that one of the numbers is divisible by 5?

29. How many consecutive numbers do you need to guarantee that one of the numbers is divisible by 6?

30. Choose a nonprime number between 900 and 1000, and find all of the factors of the number. The chart on the next page will help you select an interesting number.

24a. See right.

24b. Possible answer: They are multiples of 60.

25a. 588

25b. 1 and 588, 2 and 294, 3 and 196, 4 and 147, 6 and 98, 7 and 84, 12 and 49, 14 and 42, and 21 and 28

25c. 1×588, 2×294, 3×196, 4×147, 6×98, 7×84, 12×49, 14×42, 21×28, 28×21, 42×14, 49×12, 84×7, 98×6, 147×4, 196×3, 294×2, and 588×1

26. Three consecutive whole numbers will be either two evens with an odd in between or two odds with an even in between; Consecutive whole numbers follow the pattern odd, even, odd, even.

27. Ji Young is correct; Every third number is a multiple of 3, so every three consecutive numbers will contain a multiple of 3.

28. 5

29. 6

30. See pages 35e and 35f.

Factor Counts ■   Each * Stands for a Factor

900	**************************	951	****
901	****	952	****************
902	********	953	**
903	********	954	************
904	********	955	****
905	****	956	******
906	********	957	********
907	**	958	****
908	******	959	****
909	******	960	****************************
910	****************	961	***
911	**	962	********
912	********************	963	******
913	****	964	******
914	****	965	****
915	********	966	****************
916	******	967	**
917	****	968	************
918	****************	969	********
919	**	970	********
920	****************	971	**
921	****	972	******************
922	****	973	****
923	****	974	****
924	************************	975	************
925	******	976	**********
926	****	977	**
927	******	978	********
928	************	979	****
929	**	980	******************
930	****************	981	******
931	******	982	****
932	******	983	**
933	****	984	****************
934	****	985	****
935	********	986	********
936	**************************	987	********
937	**	988	************
938	********	989	****
939	****	990	************************
940	************	991	**
941	**	992	************
942	********	993	****
943	****	994	********
944	**********	995	****
945	****************	996	************
946	********	997	**
947	**	998	****
948	************	999	********
949	****	1000	****************
950	************		

Mathematical Reflections

In this investigation, you analyzed factor pairs. You found that factor pairs for a number are related to the rectangles that can be made from that number of square tiles. You also investigated even and odd numbers. These questions will help you summarize what you have learned:

1 Explain how the rectangles you can make using 24 tiles are related to the factor pairs of the number 24.

2 Summarize what you know about the sums and products of odd and even numbers. Justify your statements.

3 How can you tell if a number is divisible by 2? By 5? By 10?

Think about your answers to these questions, discuss your ideas with other students and your teacher, and then write a summary of your findings in your journal.

Write about your special number! What can you say about your number now? Is it even? Is it odd? How many factor pairs does it have?

Tip for the Linguistically Diverse Classroom

Diagram Code The Diagram Code technique is described in detail in *Getting to Know Connected Mathematics*. Students use a minimal number of words and drawings, diagrams, or symbols to respond to questions that require writing. Example: Question 3—A student might answer this question by writing: 2, 4, 6, 8, 0 → ÷ 2; 5, 0 → ÷ 5; 0 → ÷ 10.

TEACHING THE INVESTIGATION

3.1 • Arranging Space

In this problem, students use square tiles to build rectangles with areas of 12 and 16. They discover that the length and width of a rectangle are factors of its area.

Launch

Launch this problem by telling the story of the arts and crafts exhibit.

Explore

Let students work in pairs. To record the rectangles that they find, have students trace their tile figures or draw a representation on a sheet of grid paper. Have each pair compare its rectangles with those of another pair.

Summarize

Summarize the activity by discussing the answers to the problem. You may want to select students to present their solutions to the class. Ask students what patterns they see in the rectangles.

> What do all your rectangles for the number 12 have in common?

Here are some observations students have made:

- Tayesha observed that all the rectangles have 12 tiles.

- Kara said all the rectangles can be turned and they look different.

- Herschel said that squares are an exception to Kara's observation.

- Allen added that the edge lengths are all factors of 12.

Discuss the patterns students see in the rectangles made with 16 tiles. Some students may say that the 4×4 square is not a rectangle. You can use this opportunity to help students see that the definition of a rectangle includes squares. Note that the 4, which appears as both the length and the width of the square, is not counted as two factors; it represents only one distinct factor. Some students may see that all numbers that are not squares have an even number of factors. Square numbers have an odd number of distinct factors. If students do not see this, it will come up again in Investigation 6. You do not need to go for closure here.

3.2 • Finding Patterns

In this problem, students make rectangles for each number from 1 to 30. When all the rectangles have been displayed, students look for patterns and make observations about the rectangle models for prime, composite, square, even, and odd numbers.

Launch

Use the story in the student edition to get the students engaged in the context of the problem. Divide the class into groups, and decide how to split up the work among the groups. One strategy is to distribute prime, square, abundant, composite, and deficient numbers so that each group will have about the same amount of work to do. You may want to discuss this with your class. A more important discussion is how to divide the work within each group.

> What would be a fair way to divide the work within each group so that every member will have about an equal amount of work to do?

If you find that some students have misconceptions, such as the notion that larger numbers have more factors, keep an eye on these students during the class summary. Be sure that they are engaged in the discussion. Ask questions to assess whether they are making sense of the mathematical ideas. The class activity will likely clear up some of these misconceptions.

Explore

Have groups make displays that show all of the rectangles they found for each of their numbers. As groups finish, have them post their displays in order from 1 to 30.

As groups finish, write the following questions on the board and ask students to think about them.

- What patterns do you see in the rectangles you are making?

- What patterns do you see across all the numbers on which your group is working?

- What is the relationship between the rectangles for a number and the factors of the number?

Students who finish early may wish to extend the display beyond 30. Some of them could work on 32 or 36 as an extra challenge. Teachers who want to challenge their students further (or who have more than one grade 6 class) may extend the list to 50 or 60.

Summarize

Hold a class discussion about the patterns that students have found.

> Look at the displays of rectangles for the numbers from 1 to 30. What patterns do you notice?

Here are some observations students have made:

- Harold observed that every number is something times 1.

- Ulani said that every even number has 2 as a factor.

- Jamie said that 1 has only one rectangle—a square—and only one factor.

- Ana said that 24 and 30 have the greatest number of rectangles and, in the Factor Game, they were bad first moves.

- Whitney observed that all composite numbers have more than two rectangles because they have more than two factors, but primes have only two rectangles.

- Isaiah noticed that half of every even number is a factor of that number.

- Loren said that square numbers have an odd number of factors. Brianna added that this is because square numbers each have a number times itself as a rectangle, and this gives an odd number of factors.

Discuss with the class any questions in Problem 3.2 Follow-Up that did not come up in the discussion. Ask other questions that will help students make additional important observations. Here are examples of questions you might ask.

- What numbers between 1 and 30 are prime?

- Which pairs of primes differ by exactly 2? These are called *twin primes*.

- Which numbers have the most factors?

- Do larger numbers always have more factors than smaller numbers?

For the Teacher: Plotting the Factors

One way to help the class get the most out of their work is to work with them to make a line plot and then look for patterns and groupings. The line plot below shows the numbers from 1 to 30 on the horizontal axis. The number of Xs above each number indicates the number of factors the number has.

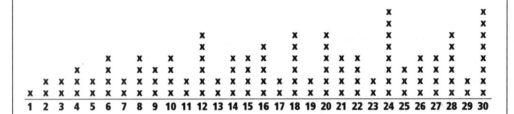

Students could record groups of numbers with the same number of factors. Students should notice that all the prime numbers have exactly two factors, all the composite numbers have more than two factors, and all the square numbers have an odd number of factors.

3.3 • Reasoning with Odd and Even Numbers

In this problem, students are introduced to tile models for odd and even numbers. They use these models, or another method they choose, to prove conjectures about sums and products of odd and even numbers.

Launch

Review the concepts of odd and even numbers with your students.

> In this problem, we will be working with odd and even numbers. Can anyone explain what makes a number even and what makes a number odd?

Students may have many ideas. Be sure the definitions on the top of page 28 of the student edition are discussed. Then, discuss and illustrate Jocelyn's tile models.

> How are the tile models for odd numbers different from the models for even numbers?

Your students should notice that the models for even numbers are rectangles with a height of 2 tiles. Models for odd numbers are rectangles with an extra tile sticking out.

In the problem, you are asked to make conjectures about the results of adding or multiplying odd and even numbers. A *conjecture* is your best guess about a relationship. For example, part A of Problem 3.3 asks you to make a conjecture about whether the sum of two even numbers is even or odd.

After you have made a conjecture, try to show why it is true. You can use Jocelyn's tile models, or you can come up with your own method.

Explore

Let students work in pairs on Problem 3.3, with each student recording the answers in his or her journal. Students who finish early can work on Problem 3.3 Follow-Up.

Summarize

Discuss the solutions, focusing not just on what happens, but on why it happens.

For the Teacher: Modeling Odd and Even Numbers

You might ask your class if they can devise another physical representation of even and odd numbers.

Additional Answers

Answers to Problem 3.1

A.

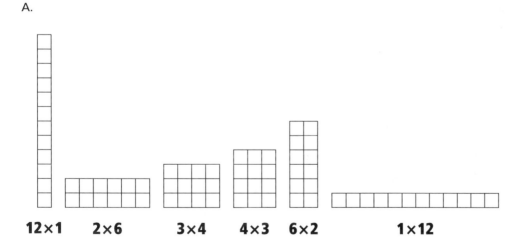

12×1   **2×6**   **3×4**   **4×3** **6×2**   **1×12**

Answers to Problem 3.3

A. The sum of two even numbers is even because we can combine two rectangles with height 2 to get another rectangle with height 2.

B. The sum of two odd numbers is even. The tile models for the odd numbers each have an extra square. If we combine the models, we can pair the extra squares to form a rectangle.

C. The sum of an odd number and an even number is odd. The model for the even number is a rectangle with height 2. The model for the odd number is a rectangle with height 2 but with an extra square. If we combine the models, we still have an extra square.

D. The product of two even numbers is even. If we combine an even number of rectangles, we get another rectangle with height 2.

E. The product of two odd numbers is odd. If we combine an odd number of rectangles with height 2 and an extra square, we get another rectangle with an extra square.

F. The product of an odd number and an even number is even. If we put together an odd number of even rectangles, we get another rectangle. And if we put together an even number of odd models, we get another rectangle.

ACE Answers

Extensions

30. Possible answers:

900	1, 2, 3, 4, 5, 6, 9, 10, 12, 15, 18, 20, 25, 30, 36, 45, 50, 60, 75, 90, 100, 150, 180, 225, 300, 450, 900	922	1, 2, 461, 922
		923	1, 13, 71, 923
901	1, 17, 53, 901	924	1, 2, 3, 4, 6, 7, 11, 12, 14, 21, 22, 28, 33, 42, 44, 66, 77, 84, 132, 154, 231, 308, 462, 924
902	1, 2, 11, 22, 41, 82, 451, 902		
903	1, 3, 7, 21, 43, 129, 301, 903	925	1, 5, 25, 37, 185, 925
904	1, 2, 4, 8, 113, 226, 452, 904	926	1, 2, 463, 926
905	1, 5, 181, 905	927	1, 3, 9, 103, 309, 927
906	1, 2, 3, 6, 151, 302, 453, 906	928	1, 2, 4, 8, 16, 29, 32, 58, 116, 232, 464, 928
908	1, 2, 4, 227, 454, 908		
909	1, 3, 9, 101, 303, 909	930	1, 2, 3, 5, 6, 10, 15, 30, 31, 62, 93, 155, 186, 310, 465, 930
910	1, 2, 5, 7, 10, 13, 14, 26, 35, 65, 70, 91, 130, 182, 455, 910		
		931	1, 7, 19, 49, 133, 931
912	1, 2, 3, 4, 6, 8, 12, 16, 19, 24, 38, 48, 57, 76, 114, 152, 228, 304, 456, 912	932	1, 2, 4, 233, 466, 932
		933	1, 3, 311, 933
		934	1, 2, 467, 934
913	1, 11, 83, 913	935	1, 5, 11, 17, 55, 85, 187, 935
914	1, 2, 457, 914	936	1, 2, 3, 4, 6, 8, 9, 12, 13, 18, 24, 26, 36, 39, 52, 72, 78, 104, 117, 156, 234, 312, 468, 936
915	1, 3, 5, 15, 61, 183, 305, 915		
916	1, 2, 4, 229, 458, 916		
917	1, 7, 131, 917	938	1, 2, 7, 14, 67, 134, 469, 938
918	1, 2, 3, 6, 9, 17, 18, 27, 34, 51, 54, 102, 153, 306, 459, 918	939	1, 3, 313, 939
		940	1, 2, 4, 5, 10, 20, 47, 94, 188, 235, 470, 940
920	1, 2, 4, 5, 8, 10, 20, 23, 40, 46, 92, 115, 184, 230, 460, 920		
		942	1, 2, 3, 6, 157, 314, 471, 942
921	1, 3, 307, 921	943	1, 23, 41, 943

944	1, 2, 4, 8, 16, 59, 118, 236, 472, 944
945	1, 3, 5, 7, 9, 15, 21, 27, 35, 45, 63, 105, 135, 189, 315, 945
946	1, 2, 11, 22, 43, 86, 473, 946
948	1, 2, 3, 4, 6, 12, 79, 158, 237, 316, 474, 948
949	1, 13, 73, 949
950	1, 2, 5, 10, 19, 25, 38, 50, 95, 190, 475, 950
951	1, 3, 317, 951
952	1, 2, 4, 7, 8, 14, 17, 28, 34, 56, 68, 119, 136, 238, 476, 952
954	1, 2, 3, 6, 9, 18, 53, 106, 159, 318, 477, 954
955	1, 5, 191, 955
956	1, 2, 4, 239, 478, 956
957	1, 3, 11, 29, 33, 87, 319, 957
958	1, 2, 479, 958
959	1, 7, 137, 959
960	1, 2, 3, 4, 5, 6, 8, 10, 12, 15, 16, 20, 24, 30, 32, 40, 48, 60, 64, 80, 96, 120, 160, 192, 240, 320, 480, 960
961	1, 31, 961
962	1, 2, 13, 26, 37, 74, 481, 962
963	1, 3, 9, 107, 321, 963
964	1, 2, 4, 241, 482, 964
965	1, 5, 193, 965
966	1, 2, 3, 6, 7, 14, 21, 23, 42, 46, 69, 138, 161, 322, 483, 966
968	1, 2, 4, 8, 11, 22, 44, 88, 121, 242, 484, 968
969	1, 3, 17, 19, 51, 57, 323, 969
970	1, 2, 5, 10, 97, 194, 485, 970
972	1, 2, 3, 4, 6, 9, 12, 18, 27, 36, 54, 81, 108, 162, 243, 324, 486, 972
973	1, 7, 139, 973
974	1, 2, 487, 974
975	1, 3, 5, 13, 15, 25, 39, 65, 75, 195, 325, 975
976	1, 2, 4, 8, 16, 61, 122, 244, 488, 976
978	1, 2, 3, 6, 163, 326, 489, 978
979	1, 11, 89, 979
980	1, 2, 4, 5, 7, 10, 14, 20, 28, 35, 49, 70, 98, 140, 196, 245, 490, 980
981	1, 3, 9, 109, 327, 981
982	1, 2, 491, 982
984	1, 2, 3, 4, 6, 8, 12, 24, 41, 82, 123, 164, 246, 328, 492, 984
985	1, 5, 197, 985
986	1, 2, 17, 29, 34, 58, 493, 986
987	1, 3, 7, 21, 47, 141, 329, 987
988	1, 2, 4, 13, 19, 26, 38, 52, 76, 247, 494, 988
989	1, 23, 43, 989
990	1, 2, 3, 5, 6, 9, 10, 11, 15, 18, 22, 30, 33, 45, 55, 66, 90, 99, 110, 165, 198, 330, 495, 990
992	1, 2, 4, 8, 16, 31, 32, 62, 124, 248, 496, 992
993	1, 3, 331, 993
994	1, 2, 7, 14, 71, 142, 497, 994
995	1, 5, 199, 995
996	1, 2, 3, 4, 6, 12, 83, 166, 249, 332, 498, 996
998	1, 2, 499, 998
999	1, 3, 9, 27, 37, 111, 333, 999
1000	1, 2, 4, 5, 8, 10, 20, 25, 40, 50, 100, 125, 200, 250, 500, 1000

Common Factors and Multiples

In this investigation, real-life situations are used to motivate students to learn about common factors and multiples. When students meet these ideas in context, it becomes clear whether the problem is asking for a common multiple, a common factor, the least common multiple, or the greatest common factor.

Problem 4.1, Riding Ferris Wheels, involves two Ferris wheels that rotate at different rates. A person gets on each Ferris wheel, and the Ferris wheels start rotating at the same time. Finding the least common multiple helps to determine when the two people will again be at the bottom together. Problem 4.2, Looking at Locust Cycles, involves a plague of 13-year and 17-year locusts that struck in 1935. Students use the least common multiple to predict when such a plague might occur again. In Problem 4.3, Planning a Picnic, students use common factors to investigate how snacks can be shared equally in a group.

Mathematical and Problem-Solving Goals

- **To recognize situations in which finding factors and multiples of whole numbers will be helpful in answering questions**

- **To observe and reason using patterns of factors and multiples**

- **To use properties of factors and multiples to explain some numerical facts about everyday life**

Materials		
Problem	**For students**	**For the teacher**
All	Calculators	Transparencies 4.1 to 4.3

Student Pages 36–45   Teaching the Investigation 45a–45c

Riding Ferris Wheels

At a Glance

Grouping:
Pairs or Small Groups

Launch

- With the class, make a list of factors for 24 and 36 and find the common factors.

- With the class, make a list of multiples for 24 and 36 and find the common multiples.

- Read Problem 4.1 aloud. Make sure the students understand what is being asked.

Explore

- Circulate as students work to solve the problem.

Summarize

- Let students share their answer and explain their thinking.

- Point out that, in part A, the answer is one of the given numbers, and, in part C the answer is the product of the two numbers.

Common Factors and Multiples

There are many things in the world that happen over and over again in set cycles. Sometimes we want to know when two things with different cycles will happen at the same time. Knowing about factors and multiples can help you to solve such problems.

Let's start by comparing the multiples of 20 and 30.

- The multiples of 20 are 20, 40, 60, 80, 100, 120, . . .
- The multiples of 30 are 30, 60, 90, 120, 150, 180, . . .

The numbers 60, 120, 180, 240, . . . are multiples of both 20 and 30. We call these numbers **common multiples** of 20 and 30.

Now let's compare the factors of 12 and 30.

- The factors of 12 are 1, 2, 3, 4, 6, and 12.
- The factors of 30 are 1, 2, 3, 5, 6, 10, 15, and 30.

The numbers 1, 2, 3, and 6 are factors of both 12 and 30. We call these numbers **common factors** of 12 and 30.

Can you figure out how many people could ride in each car?

4.1 Riding Ferris Wheels

One of the most popular rides at a carnival or amusement park is the Ferris wheel.

> **Did you know?**
>
> The largest Ferris Wheel was built for the World's Columbian Exposition in Chicago in 1893. The wheel could carry 2160 people in its 36 passenger cars.

Assignment Choices

ACE questions 1–4 and unassigned choices from earlier problems

Answer to Problem 4.1

A. The multiples of 20 are 20, 40, 60, 80, 100, ... The multiples of 60 are 60, 120, 180, 240, 300, etc. The least common multiple (the smallest number that appears on both lists) is 60. So both siblings will be on the ground again in 60 seconds.

B. 150 seconds

C. 70 seconds

Problem 4.1

You and your little sister go to a carnival that has both a large and a small Ferris wheel. You get on the large Ferris wheel at the same time your sister gets on the small Ferris wheel. The rides begin as soon as you are both buckled into your seats. Determine the number of seconds that will pass before you and your sister are both at the bottom again

A. if the large wheel makes one revolution in 60 seconds and the small wheel makes one revolution in 20 seconds.

B. if the large wheel makes one revolution in 50 seconds and the small wheel makes one revolution in 30 seconds.

C. if the large wheel makes one revolution in 10 seconds and the small wheel makes one revolution in 7 seconds.

■ **Problem 4.1 Follow-Up**

For parts A–C in Problem 4.1, determine the number of times each Ferris wheel goes around before you and your sister are both on the ground again.

Answers to Problem 4.1 Follow-Up

A. The large Ferris wheel goes around one time, and the small Ferris wheel goes around three times.

B. The large Ferris wheel goes around three times, and the small Ferris wheel goes around five times.

C. The large Ferris wheel goes around seven times, and the small Ferris wheel goes around ten times.

Looking at Locust Cycles

At a Glance

Grouping:
Pairs or Small Groups

Launch

- Remind students of the locust problem posed at the beginning of the student edition.

- Read Problem 4.2 with the students and make sure they understand the questions being asked.

Explore

- Circulate as students work on the problem.

- If students get stuck, ask them to think about how this problem is similar to the last problem.

Summarize

- Have students present their strategies and solutions.

- Point out that, in part A, the solution is the product of the two numbers, and in part B, the solution is smaller than the product of the two numbers.

Assignment Choices

ACE questions 5–7, 14–16, 18, and unassigned choices from earlier problems

---

Cicadas spend most of their lives underground. Some cicadas—commonly called 13-year locusts—come above ground every 13 years, while others—called 17-year locusts—come out every 17 years.

Problem 4.2

Stephan's grandfather told him about a terrible year when the cicadas were so numerous that they ate all the crops on his farm. Stephan conjectured that both 13-year and 17-year locusts came out that year. Assume Stephan's conjecture is correct.

A. How many years pass between the years when both 13-year and 17-year locusts are out at the same time? Explain how you got your answer.

B. Suppose there were 12-year, 14-year, and 16-year locusts, and they all came out this year. How many years will it be before they all come out together again? Explain how you got your answer.

Problem 4.2 Follow-Up

For parts A and B of Problem 4.2, tell whether the answer is less than, greater than, or equal to the product of the locust cycles.

"BELIEVE ME, THEY'LL NOT EXPECTING US. WE'RE 387-YEAR LOCUSTS."

©1991 by Sidney Harris. From *You Want Proof? I'll Give You Proof!* W.H. Freeman, New York.

Answers to Problem 4.2

A. 221 years; Possible explanation: The multiples of 13 are 13, 26, 39, 52, 65, 78, 91, 104, 117, 130, 143, 156, 169, 182, 195, 208, 221, ... The multiples of 17 are 17, 34, 51, 68, 85, 102, 119, 136, 153, 170, 187, 204, 221, ... The least common multiple is 221.

B. 336 years; Possible explanation: The multiples of 12 are 12, 24, 36, 48, 60, 72, 84, 96, 108, 120, 132, 144, 156, 168, 180, 192, 204, 216, 228, 240, 252, 264, 276, 288, 300, 312, 324, 336, ... The multiples of 14 are 14, 28, 42, 56, 70, 84, 98, 112, 126, 140, 154, 168, 182, 196, 210, 224, 238, 252, 266, 280, 294, 308, 322, 336, ... The multiples of 16 are 16, 32, 48, 64, 80, 96, 112, 128, 144, 160, 176, 192, 208, 224, 240, 256, 272, 288, 304, 320, 336, ... The least common multiple of 12, 14, and 16 is 336.

Answers to Problem 4.2 Follow-Up

A. $221 = 13 \times 17$ B. $336 < 12 \times 14 \times 16$

4.3 Planning a Picnic

Common factors and common multiples can be used to figure out how many people can share things equally.

Problem 4.3

Miriam's uncle donated 120 cans of juice and 90 packs of cheese crackers for the school picnic. Each student is to receive the same number of cans of juice and the same number of packs of crackers.

What is the largest number of students that can come to the picnic and share the food equally? How many cans of juice and how many packs of crackers will each student receive? Explain how you got your answers.

■ **Problem 4.3 Follow-Up**

If Miriam's uncle eats two packs of crackers before he sends the supplies to the school, what is the largest number of students that can come to the picnic and share the food equally? How many cans of juice and how many packs of crackers will each receive?

At a Glance

Grouping: Individuals, then Pairs

Launch

■ Read the problem to the class, and ask students to suggest how they might solve it.

■ Help students see that, to solve the problem, they need to find factors.

Explore

■ Circulate as students work on the problem.

Summarize

■ Have students present their strategies and solutions.

■ Hold a discussion about how students might start their responses to the Mathematical Reflections.

Answer to Problem 4.3

The factors of 120 are 1, 2, 3, 4, 5, 6, 8, 10, 12, 15, 20, 24, 30, 40, 60, and 120. The factors of 90 are 1, 2, 3, 5, 6, 9, 10, 15, 18, 30, 45, and 90. The greatest common factor is 30. So, 30 students can attend the picnic. Each student will receive 4 cans of juice and 3 packs of crackers.

Answer to Problem 4.3 Follow-Up

Now there are only 88 packs of crackers. The factors of 88 are 1, 2, 4, 8, 11, 22, 44, and 88. The greatest common factor of 120 and 88 is 8. So, 8 students can attend. Each student will receive 15 cans of juice and 11 packs of crackers.

Assignment Choices

ACE questions 17, 21, 22, and unassigned choices from earlier problems (Assign 19, 20, and 23 as an extra challenge.)

Answers

Applications

1. 24, 48, 72, and 96; The least common multiple is 24.

2. 15, 30, 45, 60, 75, and 90; The least common multiple is 15.

3. 77; The least common multiple is 77.

4. 90; The least common multiple is 90.

5. Possible answer: 2 and 5, 2 and 10

6. Possible answer: 4 and 9, 12 and 36

7. Possible answer: 4 and 15, 5 and 12

8. 1, 2, 3, and 6; The greatest common factor is 6.

9. 1; The greatest common factor is 1.

10. 1, 3, 5, and 15; The greatest common factor is 15.

11. Possible answer: 16 and 24, 40 and 48

12. Possible answer: 2 and 3, 9 and 16

13. Possible answer: 15 and 30, 105 and 30

As you work on these ACE questions, use your calculator whenever you need it.

Applications

In 1–4, list the common multiples between 1 and 100 for each pair of numbers. Then find the least common multiple for each pair.

1. 8 and 12

2. 3 and 15

3. 7 and 11

4. 9 and 10

In 5–7, find two pairs of numbers with the given number as their least common multiple.

5. 10

6. 36

7. 60

In 8–10, list the common factors for each pair of numbers. Then find the greatest common factor for each pair.

8. 18 and 30

9. 9 and 25

10. 60 and 45

In 11–13, find two pairs of numbers with the given number as their greatest common factor.

11. 8

12. 1

13. 15

Connections

14. Mr. Vicario and his 23 students are planning to have hot dogs at their class picnic. Hot dogs come in packages of 12, and hot dog buns come in packages of 8.

a. What is the smallest number of packages of hot dogs and the smallest number of packages of buns Mr. Vicario can buy so that everyone including him gets the same number of hot dogs and buns and there are no leftovers? How many hot dogs and buns does each person get?

b. If the class invites the principal, the secretary, the bus driver, and three parents to help supervise, how many packages of hot dogs and buns will Mr. Vicario need to buy? How many hot dogs and buns will each person get if there are to be no leftovers?

15. The school cafeteria serves pizza every sixth school day and applesauce every eighth school day. If pizza and applesauce are both on today's menu, how many school days will it be before they are both on the menu again?

16. Two neon signs are turned on at the same time. Both signs blink as they are turned on. One sign blinks every 9 seconds. The other sign blinks every 15 seconds. In how many seconds will they blink together again?

Extensions

17a. either every time they emerge or never; The 13-year locusts would encounter predators every other time they emerge, so they could be better or worse off depending on whether the predator came out on odd or even years.

17b. The 12-year locusts will meet both types of predators every time they emerge. The 13-year locusts will meet the 2-year predators every other time they emerge, and the 3-year predators every third time they emerge. This means that it will be 6 cycles or 78 years before the 13-year locusts have to face both predators again. They are better off than the 12-year locusts.

18. 90 years

19a. $1 + 3 + 5 + 7 + 9 = 25$

$1 + 3 + 5 + 7 + 9 + 11 = 36$

$1 + 3 + 5 + 7 + 9 + 11 + 13 = 49$

$1 + 3 + 5 + 7 + 9 + 11 + 13 + 15 = 64$

Extensions

17. Stephan told his biology teacher his conjecture that the terrible year of the cicadas occurred because 13-year and 17-year locusts came out at the same time. The teacher thought Stephan's conjecture was probably incorrect, because cicadas in a particular area seem to be either all 13-year locusts or all 17-year locusts, but not both. Stephan read about cicadas and found out that they are eaten very quickly by lots of predators. However, the cicadas are only in danger if their cycle occurs at the same time as the cycles of their predators. Stephan suspects that the reason there are 13-year and 17-year locusts but not 12-year, 14-year, or 16-year locusts has to do with predator cycles.

a. Suppose cicadas have predators with 2-year cycles. How often would 12-year locusts face their predators? Would life be better for 13-year locusts?

b. Suppose 12-year and 13-year locusts have predators with both 2-year and 3-year cycles. Suppose both kinds of locusts and both kinds of predators came out this year. When would the 12-year locusts again have to face both kinds of predators at the same time? What about the 13-year locusts? Which type of locust do you think is better off?

18. Suppose that in some distant part of the universe there is a star with four orbiting planets. One planet makes a trip around the star in 6 earth years, the second planet takes 9 earth years, the third takes 15 earth years, and the fourth takes 18 earth years. Suppose that at some time the planets are lined up as pictured. This phenomenon is called *conjunction*. How many years will it take before the planets return to this position?

Tip for the Linguistically Diverse Classroom

Visual Enhancement The Visual Enhancement technique is described in detail in *Getting to Know Connected Mathematics*. It involves using real objects or pictures to make information comprehensible. Example: When presenting the extension questions on this page, you might show pictures of cicadas and locusts and predators of them, as well as pictures of the solar system and universe.

19. Examine the number pattern below. You can use the tiles to help you see a pattern.

1	= 1	
1 + 3	= 4	
1 + 3 + 5	= 9	
1 + 3 + 5 + 7	= 16	

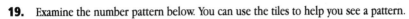

a. Complete the next four rows in the number pattern.

b. What is the sum in row 20?

c. In what row will the sum be 576? What is the last number in the sum in this row? Explain how you got your answers.

20. Examine the pattern below. Using tiles may help you see a pattern.

2	= 2
2 + 4	= 6
2 + 4 + 6	= 12
2 + 4 + 6 + 8	= 20

2 + 4 + 6

a. Complete the next four rows in the pattern.

b. What is the sum in row 20?

c. In what row will the sum be 110? What is the last number in the sum in this row? Explain how you got your answers.

21. Ms. Soong has a lot of pens in her desk drawer. She says that if you divide the total number of pens by 2, 3, 4, 5, or 6, you get a remainder of 1. What is the smallest number of pens that could be in Ms. Soong's drawer?

22. What is the mystery number pair?
Clue 1 The greatest common factor of the mystery pair is 7.
Clue 2 The least common multiple of the mystery pair is 70.
Clue 3 Both of the numbers in the mystery pair have two digits.
Clue 4 One of the numbers in the mystery pair is odd and the other is even.

Investigation 4: Common Factors and Multiples **43**

19b. $1 + 3 + 5 + \ldots + 39 = 400$.

19c. row 24; 47; The sum will be 576 in row 24, because $576 = 24^2$. The last number in this row is 47 because 47 is the twenty-fourth odd number. This famous pattern is the *sum of the consecutive odd numbers:* the sum in each row is the square of the number of numbers in the row.

20a. Tiles can be used to set up a visual display of this problem (see below left). From the pattern, you can see that adding the first *n* consecutive even numbers is the same as multiplying *n* times $(n + 1)$. So, the next four rows are as follows:

$2 + 4 + 6 + 8 + 10 = 30$ (which is 5×6)

$2 + 4 + 6 + 8 + 10 + 12 = 42$ (which is 6×7)

$2 + 4 + 6 + 8 + 10 + 12 + 14 = 56$ (which is 7×8)

$2 + 4 + 6 + 8 + 10 + 12 + 14 + 16 = 72$ (which is 8×9)

20b. $2 + 4 + 6 + \ldots + 40 = 420$ (which is 20×21)

20c. row 10; 20, because 20 is the tenth even number

21. $3 \times 4 \times 5 + 1 = 61$
22. 14 and 35

Tile pattern for question 20a:

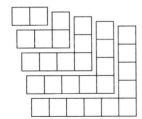

23. Possible answers:
1-4-04, 2-28-56, 3-15-45,
4-20-80, 5-18-90

23. While Min Ji was reading through her old journals, she noticed that on March 31, 1993, she had written the date 3-31-93. It looked like a multiplication problem, $3 \times 31 = 93$. Find as many other such dates as you can.

Mathematical Reflections

In this investigation, you used the ideas of common factors and common multiples to help you solve problems. These questions will help you summarize what you have learned:

1 Look at the three problems in this investigation. For which problems was it helpful to find common multiples? For which problems was it helpful to find common factors?

2 Make up a word problem you can solve by finding common factors and a different problem you can solve by finding common multiples. Solve your problems, and explain how you know your answers are correct.

3 Describe how you can find the common factors for two numbers.

4 Describe how you can find the common multiples for two numbers.

Think about your answers to these questions, discuss your ideas with other students and your teacher, and then write a summary of your findings in your journal.

Don't forget to write about your special number!

Tip for the Linguistically Diverse Classroom

Diagram Code The Diagram Code technique is described in detail in *Getting to Know Connected Mathematics*. Students use a minimal number of words and drawings, diagrams, or symbols to respond to questions that require writing. Example: Question 3—A student might answer this question by writing two numbers, listing their factors, and circling the ones in both lists.

Number	Factors
12	⑥② 4,③① 12
18	⑥③② 9,① 18

The factors that appear for both numbers are circled.

Common factors: 1, 2, 3, 6

Possible Answers

1. In the first two problems, it was helpful to find common multiples. In the last problem, it was helpful to find common factors.

2. Shauna's father's company donated 140 pencils to the class. The hotel where Jamal's mother works donated 84 notepads to the class. What is the maximum number of students a class can have for each student to share the pencils and the notepads equally? How many pencils and how many notepads will each student receive?

Solution: The factors of 140 are 1, 2, 4, 5, 7, 10, 14, 20, 28, 35, 70, and 140. The factors of 84 are 1, 2, 3, 4, 6, 7, 12, 14, 21, 28, 42, and 84. The greatest common factor of the numbers—the maximum number of students a class can have—is 28. Each student would receive 5 pencils and 3 notepads.

Jason has two different sets of model trains. One set is larger than the other. He has the tracks for each train set up in a circle on either side of a railway station building. It takes the larger train 45 seconds to go around the track. It takes the smaller train 75 seconds to go around the track. If they leave the station at the same time, how often will they be at the station at the same time?

Answers continued on page 45c.

Investigation 4 **45**

TEACHING THE INVESTIGATION

4.1 • Riding Ferris Wheels

In this problem, students use common multiples to solve a problem about riding ferris wheels.

Launch

It is important to discuss the differences and connections between factors and multiples. Ask students for the factors of 24 and the factors of 36. As students find the factors, write them on the board. When you have a list of factors for each number, ask which factors appear in both lists, and discuss what it means for a number to be in both lists. Explain that these numbers are the *common factors* of 24 and 36.

Next, ask students to find the first ten multiples of 24 and the first ten multiples of 36, and list the multiples of each number on the board. Students may not include the numbers themselves in the list. This gives you an opportunity to emphasize that the smallest multiple of any number is the number itself. When the lists are complete, ask students to find the numbers that appear on both lists. Explain that these numbers are the *common multiples* of 24 and 36. Ask what the numbers that appear on both lists have in common. Some students may see that every number that appears on both lists is divisible by 72. When you feel students are ready, move on to the problem.

> We are going to use the ideas of common factors and common multiples to solve the problems in this investigation.

Read Problem 4.1 aloud. Make sure students understand what is being asked.

Explore

Have students work in pairs or small groups to solve the problem. Remind them to record their results in their journals. If a group finishes early, have them work on Problem 4.1 Follow-Up.

Summarize

Let students share their answers and explain their thinking. You may want to spend some time having them mentally convert each answer to minutes. For example, in part B, students should realize that the siblings will both be at the bottom every two and a half minutes.

Students may notice that in part A the answer is one of the two numbers, and in part C the answer is the product of the two numbers. If students do not make these observations, prompt them:

> I noticed that in part A the answer is one of the given numbers. In part C the answer is the product of the two numbers. (*You may want to write these observations on the board.*) I wonder what is special about these numbers that made this happen. As we work on the rest of this unit, try to notice other number pairs that produce these results.

This is an important question to pose before moving on to the next problem. Although you are not ready to answer the question, if you ask it now, students may notice this pattern in other problems. This will make your work easier later on.

4.2 • Looking at Locust Cycles

In this problem, students find common multiples to predict when 13-year and 17-year locusts will be out at the same time.

Launch

Remind students of the locust problem posed at the beginning of the student edition.

> Problem 4.2 involves the 13-year and 17-year locusts described at the beginning of your book. Like the Ferris wheel problem, the locust problem involves determining when two or more things will happen at the same time.

Read Problem 4.2 with the students, and discuss the situation until you feel your students understand the questions being asked.

Explore

Have students work in pairs or small groups to explore the problem. Help them stay focused on the problem, and remind them to be ready to share their strategies as well as their solutions. If students are stuck, ask them to explore how this problem is similar to the Ferris wheel problem and to review the strategies they used to solve that problem. If you have time for presentations, have students write their responses on the board.

Summarize

Have students present their strategies and solutions. After the first group of students has shared its strategy, ask if any group has a different strategy for solving the problem. You can ask these additional questions.

> I noticed that in part A the solution is the product of the two numbers, and in part B the solution is smaller than the product of the three numbers. (*Show this if it was not shown by a student.*) Why do you suppose this happens?
>
> How can we tell whether the least common multiple will be less than or equal to the product of the numbers?

Your students may not be able to answer this. Don't push them; it is a subtle idea. If the numbers have no common factors, then the least common multiple will be the product of the numbers (for example, the least common multiple of 13 and 17 is 13×17, or 221). If the numbers have a common factor, the least common multiple will be less than the product of the numbers.

4.3 • **Planning a Picnic**

This problem is different from the first two problems because it involves factors instead of multiples. We want students to wrestle with determining what signals a situation in which finding common multiples is useful and what signals a situation in which finding common factors is useful. After this problem, you will want to ask your students to make some notes about this for their Mathematical Reflections.

Launch

Read Problem 4.3 aloud. Ask students to suggest how they might solve the problem. Students may look for multiples, because this is how they solved the earlier problems. If this occurs, help students find multiples up to the least common multiple, 360.

> Is 360 a reasonable response to the question?

If students think 360 is a reasonable answer, ask:

> 360 what?

They should see that 360 students is not a reasonable answer. Remind students that part of problem solving is asking whether the answer seems reasonable. Labeling the answer and restating it in the context of the problem helps to determine whether an answer is reasonable.

Continue to ask questions that help students see that they need to find factors of the numbers.

Explore

When you feel your students have come up with a strategy, let them work in pairs on Problem 4.3 and Problem 4.3 Follow-Up.

Summarize

Part of your strategy for this summary should be to prepare students for the Mathematical Reflections. After students have shared their solutions and strategies for Problem 4.3, discuss how they might start their responses to the Mathematical Reflections. Don't push them to write if they are not ready. Some students may need more practice with problems of this sort—practice provided in the ACE questions—before they are ready to complete the Mathematical Reflections.

Additional Answers

Mathematical Reflections

2. (*continued*) Solution: The multiples of 45 are 45, 90, 135, 180, 225, 270, ... The multiples of 75 are 75, 150, 225, 300, ... The least common multiple of 45 and 90 is 225. The trains would be at the station at the same time every 225 seconds.

3. List the factors for each number and then find the factors that are in both lists.

4. List the multiples for each number and then look for the numbers that are in both lists.

Factorizations

In this investigation, the search for longer and longer factor strings of a number leads students to discover the Fundamental Theorem of Arithmetic: a whole number can be factored, except for order, into a product of primes in exactly one way. In Problem 5.1, Searching for Factor Strings, students search for strings of factors in a puzzle. In Problem 5.2, Finding the Longest Factor String, students use factor trees as a systematic way to find prime factorizations of numbers. In Problem 5.3, Using Prime Factorizations, students learn to use prime factorizations to find greatest common factors and least common multiples. The discussion of why 1 is not a prime number is in the ACE section.

Mathematical and Problem-Solving Goals

■ **To recognize that a number may have several different factorizations but, except for order, each number greater than 1 has exactly one factorization into a product of primes (the Fundamental Theorem of Arithmetic)**

■ **To use several different strategies for finding the prime factorization of a number**

■ **To recognize primes as the building blocks of whole numbers**

Materials		
Problem	**For students**	**For the teacher**
All	Calculators	Transparencies 5.1 to 5.3 (optional)
5.1	Labsheet 5.1 (1 per student)	

Searching for Factor Strings

At a Glance

Grouping: Pairs

Launch

- Work with students to find factor strings for 360. Encourage students to lengthen the strings until they have found the longest string possible.

- Hand out Labsheet 5.1 and show students how to find and circle a factor string.

Explore

- Allow students to work alone on the puzzle for a few minutes, and then to work in pairs to complete the puzzle.

- Select students to write strings on the board.

Summarize

- Hold a class discussion about the strings on the board. Ask whether there is a longer string.

- As a class, discuss the answers to Problem 5.1 Follow-Up.

Assignment Choices

ACE questions 16, 17, 19, and unassigned choices from earlier problems

Factorizations

Some numbers can be written as the product of several different pairs of factors. For example, 100 can be written as 1×100, 2×50, 4×25, 5×20, and 10×10. It is also possible to write 100 as the product of three factors, such as $2 \times 2 \times 25$ and $2 \times 5 \times 10$. Can you find a longer string of factors with a product of 100?

5.1 Searching for Factor Strings

The Product Puzzle on Labsheet 5.1 is a number-search puzzle. Your task is to find strings of numbers with a product of 840.

The Product Puzzle

30	×	14	×	8	×	7	×	210	×
×	2	×	4	×	3	×	2	×	2
105	×	2	×	5	×	84	×	56	×
×	21	×	2	×	7	×	8	×	3
40	×	20	×	4	×	7	×	5	×
×	4	×	28	×	5	×	3	×	2
6	×	8	×	21	×	2	×	105	×
×	2	×	10	×	2	×	5	×	2
32	×	3	×	14	×	60	×	56	×
×	5	×	8	×	15	×	7	×	3

Strings Found in the Product Puzzle

$105 \times 2 \times 4$

_____

_____

_____

_____

_____

_____

_____

_____

_____

_____

_____

Problem 5.1

In the Product Puzzle, find as many factor strings for 840 as you can. A string can go around corners as long as there is a multiplication sign, ×, between any two numbers. When you find a string, draw a loop around it. Keep a record of the strings you find.

■ **Problem 5.1 Follow-Up**

1. Name two strings with a product of 840 that are not in the puzzle.
2. What is the longest string you found?
3. If possible, name a string with a product of 840 that is longer than any string you found in the puzzle. Do not consider strings that contain 1.
4. How do you know when you have found the longest possible string of factors for a number?
5. How many distinct longest strings of factors are there for a given number? Strings are distinct if they are different in some way other than the order in which the factors are listed. Do not consider strings that contain 1.

Answers to Problem 5.1 Follow-Up

1. Possible answers: 420×2, 280×3

2. Answers will vary.

3. The longest string is $2 \times 2 \times 2 \times 3 \times 5 \times 7$, which is in the puzzle.

4. If all of the numbers in a string are prime, the string is the longest possible.

5. Except for order, there is only one longest string for a given number.

5.2

Finding the Longest Factor String

At a Glance

Grouping:
Pairs

Launch

■ Work with the class to make factor trees for 360. As you make a tree on the board, students should make their own trees, starting with different pairs of factors.

■ Display the different trees for 360. Help students see that the bottom row of each tree contains the same factors.

Explore

■ As students work, encourage them to come up with other organized methods for finding the longest factorization.

Summarize

■ Select pairs of students to present their strategies for finding the longest factorizations of 600, 72, and 120.

■ Discuss the questions in Problem 5.2 Follow-Up.

■ Ask questions to help students see that the longest factor string is composed entirely of primes.

Assignment Choices

ACE questions 1–12, 21, 22, and unassigned choices from earlier problems

---

The strings of factors for a number are called *factorizations* of the number. When you search for factorizations of large numbers, it helps to keep an orderly record of your steps. One way to do this is to make a *factor tree*.

To find the longest factorization for 100, for example, you might proceed as follows:

Find two factors with a product of 100. Write 100 and then draw two "branches," with the factors at the ends. Here we start three different factor trees using the pairs 2×50, 25×4, and 10×10.

Where possible, break down each of the factors into the product of two factors. Write these factors in a new row of your tree. Draw branches to show how these factors are related to the numbers in the row above. The 2 in the first tree below does not break down any further, so we draw a single branch and repeat the 2 in the next row.

The numbers in the bottom row of the last two trees do not break down any further. These trees are complete. The bottom row of the first tree contains 25, so we complete this tree by breaking 25 into 5×5.

Notice that the bottom row of each tree contains the same factors, although the order of the factors is different. All three trees indicate that the longest factorization for 100 is $2 \times 2 \times 5 \times 5$. Think about why you cannot break this string down any further.

You can use a shortcut to write $2 \times 2 \times 5 \times 5$. In this shortcut notation, the string is written $2^2 \times 5^2$, which is read "2 squared times 5 squared." The small raised numbers are called exponents. An **exponent** tells us how many times the factor is repeated. For example, $2^2 \times 5^4$ means that the 2 is repeated twice and the 5 is repeated four times. So $2^2 \times 5^4$ is the same as $2 \times 2 \times 5 \times 5 \times 5 \times 5$.

Problem 5.2

Work with a partner to find the longest factorization for 600. You may make a factor tree or use another method. When you are finished, compare your results with the results of your classmates.

Did everyone produce the same results? If so, what is the longest factorization for 600? If not, what differences occurred?

Problem 5.2 Follow-Up

1. Find the longest factorizations for 72 and 120.
2. What kinds of numbers are in the longest factor strings for the numbers you found?
3. How do you know that the factor strings you found cannot be broken down any further?
4. Rewrite the factor strings you found for 72, 120, and 600 using shortcut notation with exponents.

Answers to Problem 5.2

$600 = 2 \times 2 \times 2 \times 3 \times 5 \times 5$; If 1s are excluded, everyone should have the same factors in their strings, although they may be in a different order.

Answers to Problem 5.2 Follow-Up

1. $72 = 2 \times 2 \times 2 \times 3 \times 3$, $120 = 2 \times 2 \times 2 \times 3 \times 5$

2. prime numbers

3. They consist of prime numbers, which have no proper factors.

4. $72 = 2^3 \times 3^2$, $120 = 2^3 \times 3 \times 5$, $600 = 2^3 \times 3 \times 5^2$

5.3

Using Prime Factorizations

At a Glance

Grouping:
Pairs or Small Groups

Launch

- Ask students to find the greatest common factor and least common multiple for 24 and 60 using any strategy they choose.

- Review Heidi's methods for finding the greatest common factor and least common multiple.

- Have students try Heidi's methods on 30 and 50, and then select some students to explain their solutions.

Explore

- Have students work in pairs or groups on Problem 5.3 and Problem 5.3 Follow-Up.

Summarize

- Have students share their results and explain how they got them.

Assignment Choices

ACE questions 13–15, 20, 23, 24, and unassigned choices from earlier problems (Assign 18 as an extra challenge.)

Assessment

It is appropriate to use Quiz B and Check-Up 2 after this problem.

5.3 Using Prime Factorizations

In Investigation 4, you found common multiples and common factors of numbers by comparing lists of their multiples and factors. In this problem, you will explore a method for finding the *greatest common factor* and the *least common multiple* of two numbers by using their prime factorizations.

Heidi says she can find the greatest common factor and the least common multiple of a pair of numbers by using their prime factorizations. The **prime factorization** of a number is a string of factors made up only of primes. Below are the prime factorizations of 24 and 60.

$$24 = 2 \times 2 \times 2 \times 3 \qquad 60 = 2 \times 2 \times 3 \times 5$$

Heidi claims that the greatest common factor of two numbers is the product of the longest string of prime factors that the numbers have in common. For example, the longest string of factors that 24 and 60 have in common is $2 \times 2 \times 3$.

$$24 = 2 \times \underline{2 \times 2 \times 3} \qquad 60 = \underline{2 \times 2 \times 3} \times 5$$

According to Heidi's method, the greatest common factor of 24 and 60 is $2 \times 2 \times 3$, or 12.

Heidi claims that the least common multiple of two numbers is the product of the shortest string that contains the prime factorizations of both numbers. The shortest string that contains the prime factorizations of 24 *and* 60 is $2 \times 2 \times 2 \times 3 \times 5$.

Contains the prime factorization of 24   Contains the prime factorization of 60

$\underline{2 \times 2 \times 2 \times 3} \times 5$ $2 \times \underline{2 \times 2 \times 3 \times 5}$

According to Heidi's method, the least common multiple of 24 and 60 is $2 \times 2 \times 2 \times 3 \times 5$, or 120.

Problem 5.3

A. Try using Heidi's methods to find the greatest common factor and least common multiple of 48 and 72 and of 30 and 54.

B. Are Heidi's methods correct? Explain your thinking. If you think Heidi is wrong, revise her methods so they are correct.

Answers to Problem 5.3

A. The prime factorization of 48 is $2 \times 2 \times 2 \times 2 \times 3$. The prime factorization of 72 is $2 \times 2 \times 2 \times 3 \times 3$. Using Heidi's method, we get a greatest common factor of $2 \times 2 \times 2 \times 3$, or 24, and a least common multiple of $2 \times 2 \times 2 \times 2 \times 3 \times 3$, or 144. The greatest common factor of 30 and 54 is 6. The least common multiple is 270.

B. Heidi's methods are correct; The product of the longest string of prime factors that the numbers share must be the greatest common factor. If you put another prime in the string, the product would not divide at least one of the numbers. The product of the shortest string of prime factors that contains all the factors of both numbers must be the least common multiple. If the product were made smaller by removing a prime factor, at least one of the numbers would no longer divide into it.

■ Problem 5.3 Follow-Up

1. The greatest common factor of 25 and 12 is 1. Find two other pairs of numbers with a greatest common factor of 1. Such pairs of numbers are said to be **relatively prime**.

2. The least common multiple of 6 and 5 is 30. Find two other pairs of numbers for which the least common multiple is the product of the numbers.

3. Find two pairs of numbers for which the least common multiple is smaller than the product of the two numbers. For example, the product of 6 and 8 is 48; the least common multiple is 24.

4. How you can tell from the prime factorization whether the least common multiple of two numbers is the product of the two numbers or is less than the product of the two numbers? Explain your thinking.

Answers to Problem 5.3 Follow-Up

1. Possible answer: 2 and 3, 18 and 25

2. Possible answer: 10 and 21, 11 and 8

3. Possible answer: 12 and 60 (the least common multiple is 60), 8 and 10 (the least common multiple is 40)

4. The least common multiple of two numbers will be less than the product of the numbers if their prime factorizations have factors in common. If the prime factorizations have no factors in common, the least common multiple will be the product of the numbers.

Answers

Applications

1. $2 \times 2 \times 3 \times 3$

2. $2 \times 2 \times 3 \times 3 \times 5$

3. $3 \times 5 \times 5 \times 7$

4. $3 \times 5 \times 11$

5. 293

6. $2 \times 2 \times 2 \times 3 \times 5 \times 7$

7. $36 = 2^2 \times 3^2$, $180 = 2^2 \times 3^2 \times 5$, $525 = 3 \times 5^2 \times 7$, $165 = 3 \times 5 \times 11$, $293 = 293$, and $840 = 2^3 \times 3 \times 5 \times 7$

8. The path is $7 \times 5 \times 2 \times 3 \times 4$.

Applications • Connections • Extensions

As you work on these ACE questions, use your calculator whenever you need it.

Applications

In 1–6, find the prime factorization of each number.

1. 36   **2.** 180   **3.** 525

4. 165   **5.** 293   **6.** 840

7. Rewrite the prime factorizations you found in problems 1–6 using the shortcut notation described on page 49.

To solve a multiplication maze, you must find a path of numbers from the entrance to the exit so that the product of the numbers in the path equals the puzzle number. No diagonal moves are allowed. Below is the solution of a multiplication maze with puzzle number 840.

Multiplication Maze 840

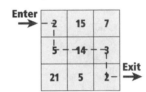

In 8 and 9, solve the multiplication maze. Hint: It may help to find the prime factorization of the puzzle number.

8.

Multiplication Maze 840

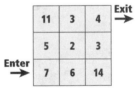

9.

Multiplication Maze 360

2	11	7
15	5	6	→ **Exit**
3	4	8

Enter →

10. Make a multiplication maze with puzzle number 720. Be sure to record your solution.

11. Find all the numbers less than 100 that have only 2s and 5s in their prime factorization. What do your notice about these numbers?

12. Find all the numbers less than 100 that are the product of exactly three different prime numbers.

In 13–15, find the greatest common factor and least common multiple for each pair of numbers.

13. 36 and 45   **14.** 30 and 75   **15.** 78 and 104

Connections

16. The number 1 is not prime. Why do you think mathematicians decided not to call 1 a prime number?

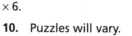

I'M #1!
I'M #1!

9. The path is $3 \times 4 \times 5 \times 6$.

10. Puzzles will vary.

11. 10, 20, 40, 50, and 80; They are all multiples of 10.

12. $2 \times 3 \times 5 = 30$, $2 \times 3 \times 7 = 42$, $2 \times 3 \times 11 = 66$, $2 \times 3 \times 13 = 78$, and $2 \times 5 \times 7 = 70$

13. greatest common factor = 9, least common multiple = 180

14. greatest common factor = 15, least common multiple = 150

15. greatest common factor = 26, least common multiple = 312

Connections

16. Mathematicians have determined that it is important for a number to be able to be identified by its longest string of factors. If the number 1 were prime, there would be no longest string of factors for a number because you could make any string longer by multiplying it by 1.

17a. 9, 18, 27, 36, 45, 54, 63, 72, 81, 90, and 99

17b. 21, 42, 63, and 84

17c. 63

17d. 126

18a. Possible answers: $1980 = 2 \times 2 \times 3 \times 3 \times 5 \times 11$, $1981 = 7 \times 283$, $1982 = 2 \times 991$, $1983 = 3 \times 661$, $1984 = 2 \times 2 \times 2 \times 2 \times 2 \times 2 \times 31$, $1985 = 5 \times 397$

18b. Answers will vary.

19. They are both correct, but Rosa's string is a more acceptable form. We do not consider 1s when we write factorizations. If we allowed 1, we could make strings as long as we wanted by adding 1s.

20. Factor to find that $184 = 8 \times 23$ and $207 = 9 \times 23$. Therefore Hiroshi worked 8 days at $23 per day and Sharina worked 9 days at $23 per day.

21. Since the number is a multiple of 2 and 7 (Clue 1), it must be a multiple of 14. The multiples of 14 between 50 and 100 (Clue 2) are $56 = 2 \times 2 \times 2 \times 7$, $70 = 2 \times 5 \times 7$, $84 = 2 \times 2 \times 3 \times 7$, and $98 = 2 \times 7 \times 7$. Of these numbers, only 70 has three different primes in its prime factorization (Clue 3). The number is 70.

22. The factors of 32 are 1, 2, 4, 8, and 16. Of these numbers, only 1 and 16 have digits that add to odd numbers (Clue 4). Of these two numbers, only 16 has 2 in its prime factorization (Clue 2). The number is 16.

---

17. **a.** Find the multiples of 9 that are less than 100.

b. Find the multiples of 21 that are less than 100.

c. Find the common multiples of 9 and 21 that are less than 100.

d. What would the next common multiple of 9 and 21 be?

18. In a and b, use the year you or one of your family members was born as your number.

a. Find the prime factorization of your number.

b. Write a paragraph describing your number to a friend, giving your friend as much information as you can about the number. Here are some things to include: Is the number square, prime, even, or odd? How many factors does it have? Is it a multiple of some other number?

19. Rosa claims the longest string of factors for 30 is $2 \times 3 \times 5$. Lon claims there is a longer string, $1 \times 2 \times 1 \times 3 \times 1 \times 5$. Who is correct? Why?

20. Hiroshi and Sharlina work on weekends and holidays doing odd jobs at the grocery store. They are paid by the day, not the hour. They each earn the same whole number of dollars per day. Last month Hiroshi earned $184 and Sharlina earned $207. How many days did each person work? What is their daily pay?

21. What is my number?
Clue 1 My number is a multiple of 2 and 7.
Clue 2 My number is less than 100 but larger than 50.
Clue 3 My number is the product of three different primes.

22. What is my number?
Clue 1 My number is a perfect square.
Clue 2 The only prime number in its prime factorization is 2.
Clue 3 My number is a factor of 32.
Clue 4 The sum of its digits is odd.

Extensions

23. Every fourth year is divided into 366 days; these years are called *leap years*. All other years are divided into 365 days. A week has 7 days.

    a. How many weeks are in a year?

    b. January 1, 1992, fell on a Wednesday. On what dates did the next three Wednesdays of 1992 occur?

    c. The year 1992 was a leap year; it had 366 days. What day of the week was January 1, 1993?

    d. What is the pattern, over several years, for the days on which your birthday will fall?

Did you know?

If you were born on any day other than February 29, leap day, it takes at least 5 years for your birthday to come around to the same day of the week. It follows a pattern of 5 years, then 6 years, then 11 years, then 6 years (or some variation of that pattern) to fall on the same day of the week. If you were born on February 29, it takes 28 years for your birthday to fall on the same day of the week!

---

24. Mr. Barkley has a box of books. He says the number of books in the box is divisible by 2, 3, 4, 5, and 6. How many books could be in the box? Add a clue so that there is only one possible solution.

Extensions

23a. 52 weeks, with 1 extra day if it is not a leap year and 2 extra days if it is a leap year

23b. January 8, 15, and 22

23c. Friday

23d. Your birthday will fall one day later in the week each year, except when leap day (February 29) falls between your birthdays. In that case, your birthday will be two days later in the week. If your birthday is February 29, your birthday will be 5 days later in the week every time it occurs.

24. The common multiples of 2, 3, 4, 5, and 6 are 60, 120, 180, ... If we add the clue that the box contains fewer than 100 books, the only answer would be 60.

Did you know?

In all of mathematics there are a few relationships that are so basic that they are called "fundamental theorems." There is the "Fundamental Theorem of Calculus," the "Fundamental Theorem of Algebra," and you have found the "Fundamental Theorem of Arithmetic." The Fundamental Theorem of Arithmetic guarantees that every whole number has exactly one longest string of primes, or prime factorization (except for the order in which the factors are written).

Mathematical Reflections

In this investigation, you found strings of factors for a number in the Product Puzzle. You learned to make a factor tree to find the prime factorization for a number. You also learned that the prime factorization of a number is the longest string of factors for the number (not including 1 as a factor). These questions will help you summarize what you have learned:

1 Why is finding the prime factorization of a number useful?

2 Describe how you would find the prime factorization of 125.

3 How can you use the prime factorization of two numbers to determine whether they are relatively prime?

4 How can you use the prime factorization of two numbers to find their common multiples?

Think about your answers to these questions, discuss your ideas with other students and your teacher, and then write a summary of your findings in your journal.

Don't forget your special number! What is its prime factorization?

Possible Answers

1. You can use the prime factorizations of two or more numbers to find common factors and multiples and the greatest common factor and least common multiple. You can also use prime factorizations to determine whether two numbers are relatively prime.

2. You could start with the factor string 5×25, then rewrite 25 as 5×5. This gives the string $5 \times 5 \times 5$. Since all the numbers in this factorization are prime, it is the prime factorization of 125.

3. Two numbers are relatively prime if their prime factorizations have no factors in common.

4. Common multiples are products of prime factor strings that contain all the factors for both numbers. For example, for the numbers 36 and 80, $36 = 2 \times 2 \times 3 \times 3$ and $80 = 2 \times 2 \times 2 \times 2 \times 5$. The shortest factor string that contains the factors of both numbers is $2 \times 2 \times 2 \times 2 \times 3 \times 3 \times 5$. The product of this string, 720, is the *least* common multiple of 36 and 80. Other common multiples are multiples of 720.

Tip for the Linguistically Diverse Classroom

Original Rebus The Original Rebus technique is described in detail in *Getting to Know Connected Mathematics*. Students make their own copy of the text before it is discussed. During discussion, they generate their own rebuses for words they do not understand as the words are made comprehensible through pictures, objects, or demonstrations. Example: Question 4 key words for which students may make rebuses are:

prime factorization: 12 broken down to $2 \times 3 \times 2$

common multiple   5: 5, ⑩ 15, ⑳
                                  10: ⑩ ⑳ 30, 40

5.1 • Searching for Factor Strings

In this problem, students search for factor strings in a puzzle.

Launch

Launch this problem by helping students to move from thinking about factor pairs to thinking about longer strings of factors.

> So far in this unit we have looked at factor pairs of given numbers. For example, we can express 30 as 1×30, 5×6, 2×15, or 3×10. Can you think of three numbers you can multiply to get a product of 30?

If students suggest a string containing a 1, such as $1 \times 2 \times 15$, ask them to suggest a different string:

> Can you find three numbers that do not include the number 1?

Students should give the string $2 \times 3 \times 5$ (they may list the factors in a different order).

> What do you think? Is this correct? Why or why not? Can you find a different string of three numbers? Why or why not?

You should not expect students to observe that all three factors in the string are primes. The focus on primes will come later in the problem.

> Let's look at a larger number because it might be more interesting. How about 360? What numbers can you multiply to get a product of 360?

Write the strings that students give you on the board, organizing them by the number of factors they contain. If students only give strings of two numbers, ask for strings of three numbers. Urge them to search for longer and longer strings. If you get answers that include 1s, just say these are not very interesting, because we can include 1s forever. If students get stuck, press them to find a strategy for lengthening the strings that are already on the board.

> How do you know when you have found the longest string possible? How do you know you cannot make a string for 360 with more numbers in it?

Here we are trying to help students think about these questions so that the search for strings in the upcoming problem will have a purpose. There will be few, if any, students who recognize that the longest string for 360 contains only prime numbers. It is not a good idea to push students to see this too soon. The Product Puzzle will give them the chance to make this observation on their own.

> We are going to continue searching for longer and longer factor strings in the Product Puzzle.

Give each student a copy of Labsheet 5.1. On Transparency 5.1, demonstrate how to draw loops around strings of numbers and record each string on the right side. The student edition shows one example, but students may need to see examples of diagonal strings and strings that loop around corners.

Point out the example in the student edition, which shows a loop around the string $105 \times 2 \times 4$. You might show students another way of drawing a loop around this string:

You might also show the loop of $8 \times 5 \times 3 \times 7$ in the mid right side of the puzzle:

However, you may want to let students make their own discoveries.

Explore

Students should work alone on the puzzle for at least five minutes, then pair up to share findings and to continue the search. Ask students to record the factors of the strings they are circling. Continue to ask whether they can find a longer string.

As you walk around the room, ask students to go to the board and list a string they have found. You may want to put headings such as "2-factor strings" and "3-factor strings" on the board to organize the strings by the number of factors. If a student is anxious to list a string already on the board but with a different ordering of the factors, either ask whether that string has already been listed, or allow it to be added to the list to stimulate conversation about the ordering of factors.

Summarize

Ask students to look carefully at the strings on the board.

> Are there any strings on the board that you disagree with? If so, why?

> The longest string we listed has ____ factors. Can you find a longer string? Why or why not?

Problem 5.1 Follow-Up should be part of this discussion. Continue to ask questions until you have a string that is composed of all primes. Because primes cannot be broken down into smaller factor pairs, an all-prime string must be the longest possible string. This might be a good time to tell your students that this factorization has a special name: it is called the *prime factorization* of the number. However, several more opportunities to make this point will present themselves as you continue this investigation, so you don't need to push the terminology now.

Some students may need more time to find a complete list (15 or more). If they can sustain their interest, have them continue their search as homework. This problem keeps students interested for a surprising length of time.

For the Teacher: A Preview of the Fundamental Theorem

The answer to question 5 in Problem 5.1 Follow-Up is the Fundamental Theorem of Arithmetic. It is revealed to students in the ACE questions, but some of your students may already have picked up on it.

5.2 • Finding the Longest Factor String

It is useful to have a systematic way to find the prime factorizations of numbers. Factor trees can help students keep their work organized.

Launch

Launch this problem by referring to previous problems.

> Yesterday we found the longest string of factors for 360. However, it would be difficult to explain how we did this to someone else because our method was not very orderly.
>
> Making a factor tree is a systematic way of finding the longest factor string for a number. Let's make some factor trees for 360. Can you tell me some factor pairs for 360?

As students call out factor pairs, list them on the board. The possible factor pairs are 36×10, 5×72, 20×18, 60×6, 2×180, 4×90, 3×120, 8×45, 9×40, 30×12, 15×24, and 1×360.

Since it is unlikely that all of the pairs listed above will be named by your students, use one they did not mention to demonstrate what a factor tree should look like. Write 360 at the top with branches leading to two factors. Have students begin their own factor trees at their desks using the factor pair they suggested or any other pair you listed on the board. Here is an example of what you might write:

> Could anyone suggest what we might do now to move us toward finding the longest possible string of factors for 360?

If students suggest "breaking apart" or "breaking down" factors that are made of other factor pairs, use their suggestion to move toward finding the longest string. If no such suggestions come from the group, ask more leading questions.

Is this the longest factor string? If not, how can I make some progress toward making it a longer string?

In the example, you might focus on 15 and ask how to break it into two factors.

Talk about what to do with numbers that are already "broken apart" as much as possible. Referring to the example, you can ask students if they can break 3 or 5 any further. When students agree they cannot, turn to 24 and ask for ways that 24 can be broken into a string of 2 factors. Continue until you have the tree shown.

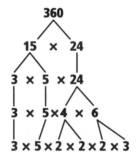

Have students continue to work on their factorization for 360 until they have found the longest possible string. Show all the factor trees that students have completed on the board.

> Did everyone get the same factorization in the bottom row of their factor tree?

Students need to recognize that, no matter what pair of factors they begin with, they will get the same longest string, except for the order of the factors. This understanding will make clear to more students that all the numbers in the bottom row are prime.

If any student has chosen the 1×360 factor pair, it should stand out among the others. This would be a good time to talk again about the redundancy of 1 as a factor.

When everyone is ready to move on, have them work in pairs on Problem 5.2.

Explore

As you circulate, continue to ask questions that lead students to work in a systematic way. Do not discourage students from developing other efficient ways to arrive at longest string. (We will soon want to refer to these longest strings as *prime factorizations*.)

When students have finished Problem 5.2, have them work on Problem 5.2 Follow-Up. These questions will give them more practice in finding prime factorizations and help them see that the longest factor string for a number is composed of prime numbers.

For the Teacher: Finding the Longest Factorization

Another way to find the longest factorization of a number is to begin by dividing by its smallest prime factor. Divide the result by its smallest prime factor. Continue in this way until the result is a prime number.

Below we show this method for 600. We started by dividing by 2, the smallest prime factor of 600. We then divided the result, 300, by 2, and so on. The prime factors are 2, 2, 2, 3, 5, and 5, so the longest factor string for 600 is $2 \times 2 \times 2 \times 3 \times 5 \times 5$.

Students might develop a similar method on their own. If some students are having difficulty making factor trees, you might want to lead them to this method. The methods are equally valid, so students should use the one that makes the most sense to them.

Summarize

Select a pair to present their strategy and the factor string they found. Ask if any pair used a different strategy or got a different result. If a student suggests a string that differs only in the order of the factors, ask if the string should really be considered different. Leave the correct longest factorization on the board so you can refer to it later.

Select two more pairs to present their factorizations for 72 and 120.

> What observations can we make about the longest factor string for a number?

Students should now begin to see that the longest factor string for a number consists entirely of prime numbers. You will probably want to continue asking questions until this point is made and discussed. If students still don't see that the strings are composed of primes, the ACE questions will provide another opportunity to explore and discuss this concept. Begin using the term *prime factorization* as soon as this idea is clear to a majority of your students.

For the Teacher: Prime Factorization

Problem 5.2 Follow-Up provides an opportunity to talk about the Fundamental Theorem of Arithmetic. Use the term prime factorization in this discussion. Students will be formally introduced to the theorem in the ACE section.

5.3 • Using Prime Factorizations

In this problem, students use prime factorizations to find greatest common factors and least common multiples.

Launch

> Take a few minutes to find the greatest common factor and the least common multiple of 24 and 60. Use any strategy you have found helpful so far.

Some students may need to refer to Investigation 4 or pair up with another student who is using a listing strategy.

When students are done, ask them to share their answers and strategies. They will most likely use a listing method. Keep a record of student strategies, especially those that are different from the majority, on the board. Refer students to page 50 in the student edition.

> Heidi has used the idea of prime factorization to develop methods for finding the greatest common factor and the least common multiple of two numbers. Let's read to see what Heidi has done with the numbers 24 and 60.

Read Heidi's strategy to the students, stopping when you need to elucidate. Engage students in a discussion about whether Heidi's methods are valid. Did she get the same answers the class did, but in a different manner? Are her methods correct, or did she just get lucky with the two numbers she chose?

Have students try Heidi's methods on 30 and 50.

Have students who are willing and confident explain Heidi's methods as applied to 30 and 50: $30 = 2 \times 3 \times 5$ and $50 = 2 \times 5 \times 5$. The common factors are 2 and 5, so the greatest common factor is $2 \times 5 = 10$. This is the largest number that will divide both 30 and 50. The smallest number that both 30 and 50 will divide into must have a 2, a 3, and two 5s in its prime factorization. Therefore, the least common multiple is $2 \times 3 \times 5 \times 5 = 150$. Students should check these results against the results obtained by using a more familiar method.

When you feel students are ready, have them work in groups or pairs on Problem 5.3 and Problem 5.3 Follow-Up.

Explore

As you circulate, ask pairs to explain their thinking about Problem 5.3 Follow-Up questions 1 and 4.

Summarize

Have students share their results and explain how they got them.

The Locker Problem

In this investigation, students use many of the properties they have learned about numbers to unravel a fanciful problem about a school with 1000 lockers.* The Locker Problem serves as a summary of the study of factors and multiples, but the skills learned in this unit should continue to develop throughout the year as students work on other problems.

Mathematical and Problem-Solving Goals

- *To use ideas about the multiplicative structure of numbers—such as primes, composites, factors, multiples, and square numbers—to solve problems*

- *To simulate a problem, gather data, make conjectures, and look for justification for those conjectures*

- *To reason mathematically and to communicate ideas clearly*

*An informative article about the Locker Problem, written by Peggy House, appears in the October 1980 issue of *Arithmetic Teacher.*

Materials		
Problem	**For students**	**For the teacher**
All	Calculators	Transparency 6.1 (optional), 12 signs denoting open and closed lockers (optional; provided as blackline masters)

Student Pages 58–64   **Teaching the Investigation 64a–64b**

Unraveling the Locker Problem

Grouping:
Small Groups

Launch

- Help students to understand the Locker Problem. You may want to demonstrate using human "lockers."

Explore

- Circulate as students work in groups on the problem.

- If students get stuck, suggest they first answer questions 1–4 of Problem 6.1 Follow-Up.

Summarize

- Ask student to explain their strategies and give their answers.

- Discuss the anwers to Problem 6.1 Follow-Up, making sure students see the connection between the lockers and the mathematics.

Assignment Choices

ACE questions 1–7, 9, 10, 12, 14, 16, and unassigned choices from earlier problems

INVESTIGATION

The Locker Problem

You have learned a lot about whole numbers in the first five investigations. In this investigation, you will use what you have learned to solve the Locker Problem. As you explore the problem, look for interesting number patterns.

6.1 **Unraveling the Locker Problem**

There are 1000 lockers in the long hall of Westfalls High. In preparation for the beginning of school, the janitor cleans the lockers and paints fresh numbers on the locker doors. The lockers are numbered from 1 to 1000. When the 1000 Westfalls High students arrive from summer vacation, they decide to celebrate the beginning of school by working off some energy.

The first student, student 1, runs down the row of lockers and opens every door.

Tip for the Linguistically Diverse Classroom

Enactment The Enactment technique is described in detail in *Getting to Know Connected Mathematics*. Students act out mini-scenes, using props, to make information comprehensible. Although enacting the locker problem on this page is presented as an option (Teaching the Investigation, page 64a), it should be required for limited English proficient students. Using the suggested cardboard doors and role-playing the opening and closing of locker doors will ensure all students' comprehension of the problem's content.

Student 2 closes the doors of lockers 2, 4, 6, 8, and so on to the end of the line.

Student 3 changes the state of the doors of lockers 3, 6, 9, 12, and so on to the end of the line. (The student opens the door if it is closed and closes the door if it is open.)

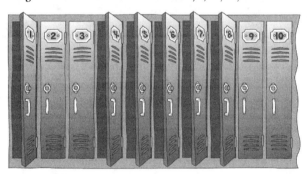

Student 4 changes the state of the doors of lockers 4, 8, 12, 16, and so on.

Student 5 changes the state of every fifth door, student 6 changes the state of every sixth door, and so on until all 1000 students have had a turn.

Investigation 6: The Locker Problem 59

Answer to Problem 6.1

Lockers with square numbers (1, 4, 9, 16, 25, 36, 49, 64, 81, 100, 121, 144, 169, 196, 225, 256, 289, 324, 361, 400, 441, 484, 529, 576, 625, 676, 729, 784, 841, 900, and 961) are open at the end.

Problem 6.1

When the students are finished, which locker doors are open?

■ **Problem 6.1 Follow-Up**

1. Work through the problem for the first 50 students. What patterns do you see as the students put their plan into action?
2. Give the numbers of several lockers that were touched by exactly two students.
3. Give the numbers of several lockers that were touched by exactly three students.
4. Give the numbers of several lockers that were touched by exactly four students.
5. Which was the first locker touched by both student 6 and student 8?
6. Which of the students touched both locker 24 and locker 36?
7. Which students touched both locker 100 and locker 120?
8. Which was the first locker touched by both student 100 and student 120?

Answers to Problem 6.1 Follow-Up

1. Answers will vary.

2. Possible answers: 2, 3, 5, 7, 11, 13, 17, 19, 23

3. Possible answers: 4, 9, 25, 49, 121, 169, 289, 361, 529, 841, 961

4. Possible answers: 6, 8, 10, 15, 27, 35

5. 24 (the least common multiple of 6 and 8)

6. 1, 2, 3, 4, 6, and 12 (the common factors of 24 and 36)

7. 1, 2, 4, 5, 10, and 20 (the common factors of 100 and 120)

8. 600

As you work on these ACE questions, use your calculator whenever you need it.

Applications

1. What is the first prime number greater than 50?

2. Ivan said that if a number ends in 0, both 2 and 5 are factors of the number. Is he correct? Why?

3. Prime numbers that differ by 2, such as 3 and 5, are called *twin primes*. Find five pairs of twin primes that are greater than 10.

4. What is my number?
Clue 1 My number is a multiple of 5 and is less than 50.
Clue 2 My number is between a pair of twin primes.
Clue 3 My number has exactly 8 factors.

5. What is my number?
Clue 1 My number is a multiple of 5, but it does not end in 5.
Clue 2 The prime factorization of my number is a string of three numbers.
Clue 3 Two of the numbers in the prime factorization are the same.
Clue 4 My number is bigger than the seventh square number.

6. Now it's your turn! Make up a set of clues for a mystery number. You might want to use your special number as the mystery number. Include as many ideas from this unit as you can. Try out your mystery number on a classmate.

7. **a.** Find all the numbers between 1 and 1000 that have 2 as their only prime factor.

   b. What is the next number after 1000 that has 2 as its only prime factor?

8. The numbers 2 and 3 are prime, consecutive numbers. Are there other such pairs of *adjacent primes*? Why or why not?

Answers

Applications

1. 53

2. yes; Numbers that end in 0 are multiples of 10. Multiples of 10 have 2 and 5 as factors.

3. Possible answers: 11 and 13, 17 and 19, 29 and 31, 41 and 43, 59 and 61

4. The multiples of 5 that are less than 50 (Clue 1) are 5, 10, 15, 20, 25, 30, 35, 40, and 45. Of these numbers, only 30 is between a pair of twin primes (Clue 2). The number is 30.

5. Since the number is a multiple of 5, but does not end in 5 (Clue 1), it must be a multiple of 10. Therefore, two of the numbers in the prime factorization are 2 and 5. Since two of the numbers in the prime factorization are the same (Clue 3), the number must be $2 \times 2 \times 5 = 20$, or $2 \times 5 \times 5 = 50$. Of these numbers, only 50 is greater than 49, the seventh square number (Clue 4). The number is 50.

6. Answers will vary.

7a. 2, 4, 8, 16, 32, 64, 128, 256, and 512

7b. 1024

8. no; A pair of consecutive numbers must contain an even number and an odd number. Since 2 is the only even prime number, 2 and 3 are the only adjacent primes.

Connections

9. multiples of 6

10. multiples of 15

11. With a square number like 16, you know you have reached the halfway point when you reach the square root, 4. After 4, the other half of the earlier factor pairs appears.

1, 2, **4**, 8, 16

This is true for nonsquare numbers as well, even though the square root is not a factor of the number. The square root of the number still can serve as a midpoint that all the factor pairs surround. For example, the square root of 12 is 3.464 . . . , and you can see that all of the factors before this number have a partner after this number.

1, 2, 3, (**3.464 . . .**), 4, 6, 12

12. odd; The only even prime is 2.

13. The square numbers between 1 and 1000 are 1, 4, 9, 16, 25, 36, 49, 64, 81, 100, 121, 144, 169, 196, 225, 256, 289, 324, 361, 400, 441, 484, 529, 576, 625, 676, 729, 784, 841, 900, and 961. Each of these numbers has an odd number of factors.

Connections

In 9 and 10, describe the numbers that have both of the given numbers as factors.

9. 2 and 3   **10.** 3 and 5

11. If you find the factors of a number by starting with 1 and finding every factor pair, you will eventually find that the factors start to repeat. For example, if you used this method to find the factors of 12, you would find that, after checking 3, you get no new factors.

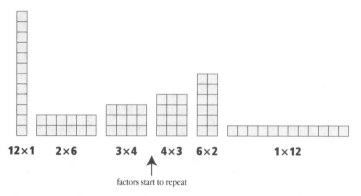

For a given number, how do you determine the largest number you need to check to make sure you have found all the factors?

Hint: It may help to first determine the answer for one or two small numbers. For example, you could look at 12 and 16. How would you know, without checking every number, that you will find no new factor pairs for 12 after checking 3? How would you know, without checking every number, that you will find no new factor pairs for 16 after checking 4? It may help to look at the rectangles you made for these numbers.

12. Which group of numbers—evens or odds—contains more prime numbers? Why?

13. Based on what you found out in the Locker Problem, make a conjecture about the number of factors for square numbers. Test this conjecture on all of the square numbers from 1 to 1000.

14. Goldbach's Conjecture is a famous conjecture that has never been proven true or false. The conjecture states that every even number, except 2, can be written as the sum of two prime numbers. For example, 16 can be written as 5 + 11, which are both prime numbers.

a. Write the first six even numbers larger than 2 as the sum of two prime numbers.

b. Write 100 as the sum of two primes.

c. The number 2 is a prime number. Can an even number larger than 4 be written as the sum of two prime numbers if you use 2 as one of the primes? Why or why not?

Extensions

15. Can you find a number less than 200 that is divisible by four different prime numbers? Why or why not?

16. In question 3, you listed five pairs of twin primes. Starting with the twin primes 5 and 7, look carefully at the numbers between twin primes. What do they have in common? Why?

17. Adrianne had trouble finding all the factors of a number. If the number was small enough, such as 8, she had no problem. But with a larger number, such as 120, she was never sure she had found all the factors. Albert told Adrianne that he had discovered a method for finding all the factors of a number by using its prime factorization. Try to discover a method for finding all the factors of a number using its prime factorization. Use your method to find all the factors of 36 and 480.

18. If a number has 2 and 6 as factors, what other numbers must be factors of the number? What is the smallest this number can be? Explain your answers.

19. If a number is a multiple of 12, what other numbers is it a multiple of? Explain your answer.

20. If 10 and 6 are common factors of two numbers, what other factors must the numbers have in common? Explain your answer.

14a. 4 = 2 + 2, 6 = 3 + 3, 8 = 3 + 5, 10 = 3 + 7 or 5 + 5, 12 = 5 + 7, and 14 = 7 + 7 or 3 + 11

14b. Possible answer: 100 = 3 + 97

14c. no; The only even prime number is 2. If you added 2 to an odd prime, the sum would be odd.

Extensions

15. no; The smallest number divisible by four different prime numbers is $2 \times 3 \times 5 \times 7 = 210$.

16. They are divisible by 6; since two twin prime numbers are not divisible by 2, the number between them must be. Similarly, the two twin primes are not divisible by 3. But, one number in every three consecutive numbers is divisible by 3, the numbers between the primes must be divisible by 3, also.

17. See page 64b.

18. 1 and 3; 6; The smallest number with 1, 2, 3, and 6 as factors is 6.

19. 1, 2, 3, 4, and 6; Since 12 is a multiple of these numbers, any multiple of 12 is also a multiple of these numbers.

20. 1, 2, 3, and 5; If 10 and 6 are factors, the factors of 10 and 6 must also be factors.

Possible Answers

1. closed; A prime number has only two factors, the number itself and 1. Therefore the lockers with prime numbers would be opened by student 1 and closed by the person with the prime number.

2. Lockers with square numbers (1, 4, 9, 16, 25, 36, 49, 64, 81, 100, 121, 144, 169, 196, 225, 256, 289, 324, 361, 400, 441, 484, 529, 576, 625, 676, 729, 784, 841, 900, and 961) were open at the end; Square numbers have an odd number of factors.

3. Factors come in pairs. Since square numbers have one factor that is paired with itself, they have an odd number of total factors.

4. Possible answer: There are 50 lockers in a hall at Phillips Middle School. Three students on Ms. Lee's team decide they will hide a treat for all the students in one of the lockers. All the lockers are closed, so the other students have to figure out which locker holds the treats without opening them. Ms. Lee gives them the following clues:

Clue 1
The locker number is even.

Clue 2
The locker number is divisible by 3.

Clue 3
The locker number is divisible by 7.

Mathematical Reflections

In this investigation, you solved a problem about open and closed lockers. Then you analyzed relationships among the lockers and the students who touched those lockers. These questions will help you summarize what you have learned:

1 Were lockers with prime numbers open or closed at the end? Explain your answer.

2 Which lockers were open at the end? Why were they open?

3 If factors come in pairs, how can a number have an odd number of factors?

4 Write a problem about students and lockers that can be solved by finding a common multiple.

Think about your answers to these questions, discuss your ideas with other students and your teacher, and then write a summary of your findings in your journal.

Don't forget your special number. What new things can you say about your number?

Tip for the Linguistically Diverse Classroom

Original Rebus The Original Rebus technique is described in detail in *Getting to Know Connected Mathematics*. Students make their own copy of the text before it is discussed. During discussion, they generate their own rebuses for words they do not understand as the words are made comprehensible through pictures, objects, or demonstrations. Example: Question 3 key words for which students may make rebuses are: *factors* (2×3; 4×5), *pairs* (pair of shoes), *number* (#), *odd number* (3, 5, 7, 9).

6.1 • Unraveling the Locker Problem

In this problem, students apply the properties they have learned about numbers to solve a problem about a school with 1000 lockers.

Launch

One way to launch this problem is by having the class act out the situation for the first 12 lockers. Use sheets of paper or cardboard with an open door on one side of each sheet and a closed door on the other (blackline masters of the lockers are provided). Number the lockers from 1 to 12. Select 12 students to be the lockers (to hold the signs). To start, students should display the closed side of each sign. Select 12 other students to be students 1 through 12. Each student, in turn, should touch the appropriate "lockers" as described in the problem. When a student holding a sign is touched, he or she should flip the sign over. This is how the lockers should look after each of the 12 students has taken a turn:

If students are having trouble understanding what is happening, you can record each step on the board in a chart something like this:

Locker

	1	2	3	4	5	6	7	8	9	10	11	12
Janitor	C	C	C	C	C	C	C	C	C	C	C	C
1	O	O	O	O	O	O	O	O	O	O	O	O
2	O	C	O	C	O	C	O	C	O	C	O	C
3	O	C	C	C	O	O	O	C	C	C	O	O
4	O	C	C	O	O	O	O	O	C	C	O	C
5	O	C	C	O	C	O	O	O	C	O	O	C
6	O	C	C	O	C	C	O	O	C	O	O	O
7	O	C	C	O	C	C	C	O	C	O	O	O
8	O	C	C	O	C	C	C	C	C	O	O	O
9	O	C	C	O	C	C	C	C	O	O	O	O
10	O	C	C	O	C	C	C	C	O	C	O	O
11	O	C	C	O	C	C	C	C	O	C	C	O
12	O	C	C	O	C	C	C	C	O	C	C	C

(Student)

Other teachers help students understand the problem, but do not suggest a way to tackle it, leaving this for the groups of students to decide. One problem-solving strategy that works well is solving an easier (smaller) problem and finding a pattern.

Explore

Divide students into groups to work on the problem. If a group is having difficulty, suggest that they look at questions 1–4 in Problem 6.1 Follow-Up and then return to the problem.

Summarize

Ask students to explain their strategies. To solve this problem, students must recognize that a locker is touched by each student whose number is a factor of that locker's number. For example, locker 18 is touched by students 1, 2, 3, 6, 9, and 18. For every pair of students that touches a locker, the locker door's state is changed twice. Since the lockers start out closed, lockers that are touched an even number of times will end up closed, and lockers that are touched an odd number of times will end up open. Since factors occur in pairs, it may seem that all the doors should end up closed. However, for a square number, one of the pairs consists of a number paired with itself. This factor pair produces only one distinct factor. Therefore, lockers with square numbers will be touched an odd number of times and will end up open.

Discuss the answers to Problem 6.1 Follow-Up. Ask students to translate the questions from the language of lockers to the language of mathematics. For example, question 6 asks, "Which of the students touched both locker 24 and locker 36?" In mathematical language, the question would be, "What are the common factors of 24 and 36?" Making this connection between the concrete setting of lockers and the mathematical underpinning is essential. After your students have had some success moving between these two representations of the questions, give them a chance to write other pairs of questions—locker and mathematical—that can be answered by analyzing the Locker Problem.

Additional Answers

ACE Answers

Extensions

17. To find all the factors of a number, find every possible combination of the number in its prime factorization. The prime factorization of 36 is $2 \times 2 \times 3 \times 3$. To find all the factors of 36, use every combination of up to two 2s, and up to two 3s. These are 2, 2×2, 3, 3×3, 2×3, $2 \times 2 \times 3$, $2 \times 3 \times 3$, and $2 \times 2 \times 3 \times 3$. The prime factorization of 480 is $2 \times 2 \times 2 \times 2 \times 2 \times 3 \times 5$. The factors are 2, 2×2, $2 \times 2 \times 2$, $2 \times 2 \times 2 \times 2$, $2 \times 2 \times 2 \times 2 \times 2$, 3, 2×3, $2 \times 2 \times 3$, $2 \times 2 \times 2 \times 3$, $2 \times 2 \times 2 \times 2 \times 3$, $2 \times 2 \times 2 \times 2 \times 2 \times 3$, 5, 2×5, $2 \times 2 \times 5$, $2 \times 2 \times 2 \times 5$, $2 \times 2 \times 2 \times 2 \times 5$, $2 \times 2 \times 2 \times 2 \times 2 \times 5$, 3×5, $2 \times 3 \times 5$, $2 \times 2 \times 3 \times 5$, $2 \times 2 \times 2 \times 3 \times 5$, $2 \times 2 \times 2 \times 2 \times 3 \times 5$, and $2 \times 2 \times 2 \times 2 \times 2 \times 3 \times 5$.

The Unit Project

My Special Number

At the beginning of this unit, you chose a special number and wrote several things about it in your journal. As you worked through the investigations, you used the concepts you learned to write new things about your number.

Now it is time for you to show off your special number. Write a story, compose a poem, create a poster, or find some other way to highlight your number. Your teacher will use your project to determine how well you understand the concepts in this unit, so be sure to include all the things you have learned while working through the investigations. You may want to start by looking back through your journal to find the things you wrote after each investigation. In your project, be sure you use all the vocabulary your teacher has asked you to record in your journal for *Prime Time*.

The unit project, My Special Number, is an integral part of the assessment in *Prime Time*. The project was introduced at the beginning of the unit. Students were asked to choose a number between 10 and 100 and to write several things about it. After each investigation, students were reminded to use the concepts they learned to write more information about their special numbers.

The project is formally assigned here. Each student should decide what form his or her project will take—such as a report, a poem, a story, or a poster. You might suggest that students locate books about numbers in the library. Many books are available that could stimulate ideas. Stress that you expect them to use the vocabulary and concepts from the unit to show everything they know about their special numbers and about what they have learned. Although students should be encouraged to be clever and creative, the emphasis of the project should be on mathematical content.

Samples of student projects and a suggested scoring rubric are given in the Assessment Resources section.

Tip for the Linguistically Diverse Classroom

Chart Summary The Chart Summary technique is described in detail in *Getting to Know Connected Mathematics*. This technique involves presenting information by condensing it in a pictorial chart with minimal words. Example: The student's special number project could be organized in a chart with headings such as Prime (or Composite), Shape, Proper Factors, Abundant (or Deficient or Perfect), Common Factors, Common Multiples. Under each of these headings, the student then uses symbols and/or drawings to illustrate how his or her special number related to each category. For example, if a student's special number was 12, he or she could write the following under the Abundant heading:

Factors of 12: 1, 2, 3, 4, 6

$$1 + 2 + 3 + 4 + 6 = 16$$
and 16 > 12

Answers

Using Your Understanding of Numbers

1a. There are six factor pairs for 60, but since 1×60 and 60×1 are different arrangements for a spectator looking at the band, there are twelve arrangements. The twelve rectangles have dimensions
1×60 2×30 3×20
4×15 5×12 6×10
60×1 30×2 20×3
15×4 12×5 10×6

b. Since 61 is prime, the only two arrangements possible are 1×61 and 61×1.

2a. Yes, during the 30th week of use.

b. Yes, during the 24th week of use.

3a. The LCM is 9900.

b. The GCF is 3.

c. The factors of Meredith's special number are 1, 2, 3, 4, 6, 11, 12, 22, 33, 44, 66, and 132.

d. A number is even if the prime factor 2 occurs in the prime factorization of the number. If 2 is not in the prime factorization, then the number is odd. So Meredith's number is even, and Elizabeth's number is odd.

e. A number is a square number if each prime factor occurs an even number of times in the prime factorization of the number. Elizabeth's number is a square number since the prime factors 3 and 5 occur twice each. Meredith's number is not a square number.

4. See page 66a.

Unit Reflections

While working on the problems in this unit, you investigated some important properties of whole numbers. Finding *factors* and *multiples* of numbers and identifying *prime numbers* helped in answering questions about clocks and calendars, puzzles and games, and rectangular patterns of tiles. Factoring also focused attention on the properties of *even* and *odd* numbers, *square* numbers, *greatest common factors*, and *least common multiples*.

Using Your Understanding of Numbers — Test your understanding of factors, multiples, and prime numbers on these problems where number patterns are the keys to solutions.

1 *The Mystate University marching band consists of 60 members. The band director wants to arrange the band into a rectangular array for the half-time activities.*

   a. How many ways can she arrange the band? Make a sketch of each arrangement.

   b. How many rectangular arrangements are possible if the band adds one member and becomes a 61-member band?

2 *The Red Top Taxi company wants to keep its cars in good operating condition, so it has a schedule for regular maintenance checks on each car. Oil is to be changed once every 6 weeks, and brakes are to be inspected and repaired every 10 weeks.*

   a. When a new cab is put in service, is there ever a week when that cab is scheduled for both an oil change and a brake inspection? If so, what is the first such time?

   b. If the oil change time is extended to 8 weeks and the brake inspection to 12 weeks, is there ever a week when the cab is due for both oil change and brake inspection? If so, when will such a coincidence occur?

3 *The prime factorization of Meredith's special number is $2 \times 2 \times 3 \times 11$ and the prime factorization of Elizabeth's special number is $3 \times 3 \times 5 \times 5$.*

   a. What is the least common multiple of the two special numbers?

   b. What is the greatest common factor of the two special numbers?

How to Use
Looking Back and Looking Ahead: Unit Reflections

The first part of this section includes problems that allow students to demonstrate their mathematical understandings and skills. The second part gives them an opportunity to explain their reasoning. This section can be used as a review to help students stand back and reflect on the "big" ideas and connections in the unit. This section may be assigned as homework, followed up with class discussion the next day. Focus on the *Explaining Your Reasoning* section in the discussion. Encourage the students to refer to the problems to illustrate their reasoning.

c. List all the factors of Meredith's special number.

d. Is Meredith's special number even or odd? How about Elizabeth's special number?

e. Is Meredith's special number a square number? Elizabeth's?

(4) *Andrea gave three clues for her secret number.*

> *Clue 1: My number is a factor of 90.*

Can you tell what Andrea's secret number is?

a. What is the smallest Andrea's number can be? What is the largest her number can be?

b. Brandon says the secret number must also be a factor of 180. Is he correct?

> *Clue 2: My number is prime.*

c. Now can you tell what the secret number is?

> *Clue 3. Twenty-one is a multiple of my secret number.*

d. Now can you tell what the secret number is?

Explaining Your Reasoning— To answer Problems 1–4 you had to use knowledge of factors and multiples of a number.

1. What strategies can be used to find

    a. all the factors of a number?   **b.** the least common multiple of two numbers?

    c. the greatest common factor of two numbers?

2. How you can you decide whether a number is a(n)

    a. prime number?   **b.** square number?

    c. even number?   **d.** odd number?

3. Which of the following statements are *always true*, which are *never true*, and which are *sometimes true*. Explain your reasoning.

    a. If a number is greater than a second number, then the first number has more factors than the second number.

    b. The sum of two odd numbers is even.

    c. The product of an even number and an odd number is odd.

    d. The least common multiple of two different prime numbers is their product.

    e. The greatest common factor of two numbers is less than either of those numbers.

You will use ideas about factors, multiples, and primes in many future units, especially those that deal with properties of other numbers like fractions and decimals.

4. No, this clue is not enough since 90 has several factors.

  a. The least possible secret number is 1. The greatest possible secret number is 90.

  b. Brandon is correct. Since the secret number is a factor of 90 and 90 is a factor of 180, then the secret number is a factor of 180.

  c. Clue 2 is still not enough to determine the number since 90 has three prime factors—2, 3 and 5.

  d. Yes, since 21 is a multiple of 3 but not a multiple of 2 or 5.

Answers

Explaining Your Reasoning

1a.
- Find all of the factor pairs (stopping when the pairs start to repeat).
- Use the prime factorization of the number.
- Use clues such as is the number even, odd, a multiple of 5 or 10 to start a list of the factors.
- Make rectangles whose dimensions are the factor pairs of the number.

Answers continue on page 66b.

For the Teacher: Finding Factor Pairs

A point to discuss when you are finding the factor pairs (or a list of factors) is "How far must you check before you are sure that you have found all of the factors?" Students start with 1 and then continue to check each of the whole numbers in order until the factor pairs begin to repeat. The square root of the original number is between the first two repeating numbers. For example, to find all of the factor pairs of 60, you need only check the whole numbers 1 through 7. The square root of 60 is between 7 and 8.

Looking Back and Looking Ahead
Possible Answers

1b. Make a list of the multiples of each number starting with the number itself. The least common multiple is the first multiple to appear in each list. For example, in Problem 3, the multiples of X are 132, 264, 396, 528, 660, 792, 924, 1056, 1188, 1320, 1452, 1580, 1716, 1848, 1980, 2112, ...9768, **9900**, 10032, ...
The multiples of Y are 225, 450, 675, 900, 1125, 1350, 1575, 1800, 2025, ...9675, **9900**, 10125, ...

Use the prime factorization. The LCM must contain each of the primes that occur in either number. The prime factor must occur the maximum number of times it occurred in either number. For example, in Problem 4, the LCM of X and Y is $2 \times 2 \times 3 \times 3 \times 5 \times 5 \times 11$ or 9900.

Discussing both strategies may reveal that the prime factorization may be the most efficient method for finding the LCM. Also refer to Problem 2 which is an application that involves finding the LCM of two numbers.

c. List all of the factors of each number and then find the greatest factor that is common to both lists. For example, in Problem 3, the factors of X are 1, 2, **3**, 4, 6, 11, 12, 22, 33, 44, 66, and 132. The factors of Y are 1, **3**, 5, 9, 15, 25, 75, and 225.

Use the prime factorization. The GCF must contain all of the prime factors that occur in each number. In Problem 3, the GCF is 3. It is the only prime that occurs in both numbers.

2a. A number is prime if it has no factors other than 1 and itself. One way to do this is to list all of the factors of the numbers.

b. A number is square if its prime factorization contains each prime factor an even number of times. See Problem 3e for an example. Some students will find all the factors and decide that if the number has an odd number of factors, then it is a square number. Some students may guess and check to see if the number has a factor pair that contains two equal factors. In this case they need to only check numbers 1 to the whole number that is the closest to the square root of the number. Some students may suggest using the square root button on a calculator. Some may say it is square if you can make a square whose area (number of unit tiles) is the number.

c. A number is even if 2 is a factor of the number.

d. A number is odd if 2 is not a factor of the number.

3a. Sometimes true. For example, if the two numbers are 15 and 11, then 15 is greater than 11, but 15 has more factors than 11. If the two numbers are 15 and 12, then 15 is greater than 12, but 15 does not have more factors than 12.

b. Always true. An odd number has an even number of groups of two with one leftover and each even number has an even number of twos. If the two odd numbers are added, the leftovers from each number combine to form a group of two resulting in have an even number of twos. Therefore the sum is even. An illustration to explain reasoning should show that the odd pieces in each odd number combine to form a group of two.

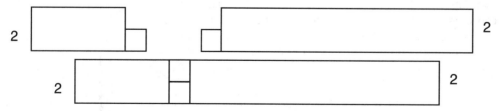

Note to the Teacher:
If X and Y are even, then $X = 2N$ and $Y = 2M$ where N and M are whole numbers. Thus, $X + Y = 2N + 2M = 2(N + M)$. So the sum is even.

3c. Always false. Students may use a geometric argument using rectangular arrangements. For example, $4 \times 3 = 12$. You have four rows of 3. Thus the product contains 4 groups of 3 which make an even number of threes in the product.

Note to the Teacher:

If X is even, then $X = 2N$. If Y is odd, then $Y = 2M + 1$.

Then $XY = 2N(2M + 1)$. This shows that 2 is a factor of XY and thus XY is even.

d. Always true. For example, if the two numbers are 5 and 17, then the LCM must contain all of the proper factors of 5 and 17, but since both are prime, then LCM $= 5 \times 17$.

Note to the Teacher:

The above reasoning is similar to the following general argument. If x and y are prime, x is the only factor of x other than one, and y is the only factor of y other than one. Therefore, the first common multiple with both x and y as factors is xy.

e. Sometimes true. If one of the numbers is a factor of the other, it is the greatest common factor of the two. For example, if $x = 6$ and $y = 12$, then the GCF of 6 and 12 is 6. And 6 is not less than 6. But if $x = 12$ and $y = 18$, then the GCF is 6 and 6 is less than both 12 and 18.

Assessment Resources

Check-Up 1

In 1 and 2, list all the factors of each number.

1. 35

2. 54

In 3 and 4, list all the proper factors of each number.

3. 42

4. 47

5. Which of the numbers in questions 1–4 are prime numbers?

6. Which of the numbers in questions 1–4 are composite numbers?

7. Which of the numbers in questions 1–4 are even numbers?

8. Is the sum of an odd number and an even number odd or even? Explain.

Quiz A

1. Suppose you are playing the Factor Game on the 30-board. Your opponent goes first and chooses 29, giving you only 1 point. It is now your turn to choose a number. Which number would be your best move? Why?

2. Suppose the person who sits next to you was absent the day you played the Factor Game. On the back of this paper, write a note to him or her explaining the strategies you have discovered for winning the Factor Game. Include a description of how you decide which move to make when it is your turn.

3. A Product Game board has this product grid.

4	6	8	9
12	16	18	24
27	32	36	48
54	64	72	?

   a. What factors would you need in order to play the game using this board?

   b. What product is missing?

4. Terrapin Crafts wants to rent between 30 and 50 square yards of space for a big crafts show. The space must be rectangular, and the side lengths must be whole numbers.

   a. Which number(s) of square yards, between 30 and 50, would give them the greatest number of rectangular arrangements to choose from?

   b. Which number(s) of square yards, between 30 and 50, would allow them to have a square space in which to set up their booth?

Check-Up 2

In 1–4, list all the factor pairs for each number.

1. 18

2. 25

3. 36

4. 48

In 5 and 6, list all the common factors for each pair of numbers.

5. 36 and 48

6. 25 and 36

In 7–10, list the first ten multiples of each number.

7. 18

8. 25

9. 36

10. 48

11. Use your lists from questions 9 and 10 to find the common multiples of 36 and 48.

12. Find a common multiple of 36 and 48 that is not in your lists.

In 13–15, write the prime factorization of each number.

13. 48

14. 95

15. 120

16. Jill says 6 is a common factor of 56 and 36. Is she correct? Explain your reasoning.

Quiz B

1. Vicente made three dozen cookies for the student council bake sale. He wants to package them in small bags with the same number of cookies in each bag.

   a. List all the ways Vicente can package the cookies.

   b. If you were Vicente, how many cookies would you put in each bag? Why?

   c. Vicente spent $5.40 on ingredients for the cookies. The student council will pay him back for the money he spent. For each of the answers you have for part a, determine how much the student council should charge for each bag of cookies so they make a profit yet still get students to buy the cookies.

2. Two radio stations are playing the number 1 hit song "2 Nice 2 B True" by Anita and the Goody-2-Shoes. WMTH plays the song every 18 minutes. WMSU plays the song every 24 minutes. Both stations play the song at 3:00 P.M.

   a. When is the next time the stations will play the song at the same time?

   b. When is the next time they will both play the song at the top of the hour?

3. List four pairs of numbers whose least common multiple is the same as their product. For example, the least common multiple of 5 and 6 is 30.

4. List four pairs of numbers whose least common multiple is smaller than their product. For example, the least common multiple of 6 and 9 is 18.

5. For a given pair of numbers, how can you tell whether the least common multiple will be less than or equal to their product?

6. Judith is planning a party for her younger brother. She has 36 prizes and 24 balloons. How many children can she have at the party so that each child gets an equal number of prizes and an equal number of balloons? Explain your answer.

Assign these questions as additional homework, or use them as review, quiz, or test questions.

1. Scarlett and Rhett were playing the Factor Game when Ashley looked over and saw that the numbers 1 to 15 were all circled. Ashley immediately said, "Oh, I see that your game is over." Is Ashley correct? Explain your answer.

In 2–4, describe how you can tell whether a given number is a multiple of the number shown.

2. 2   3. 3   4. 5

5. List all multiples of 6 between 1 and 100. What do these numbers have in common?

6. Mr. Matsumoto said, "I am thinking of a number. I know that to be sure I find all of the factor pairs of this number, I have to check all the numbers from 1 through 15."

   a. What is the smallest number he could be thinking of? Explain your answer.

   b. What is the largest number he could be thinking of? Explain your answer.

7. What is the mystery number?

   Clue 1 My number is between the square numbers 1 and 25.

   Clue 2 My number has exactly two factors.

   Clue 3 Both 66 and 605 are multiples of my number.

8. Use concepts you have learned in this unit to create a mystery number question. Each clue must contain at least one word from your vocabulary list.

9. a. List the first ten square numbers.

   b. Give all the factors for each number you listed in part a.

   c. Which of the square numbers you listed have only three factors?

   d. If you continued your list, what would be the next square number with only three factors?

10. A mystery number is greater than 50 and less than 100. You can make exactly five different rectangles with the mystery number of tiles. Its prime factorization consists of only one prime number. What is the number?

11. A number has 4 and 5 as factors.
    a. What other numbers must be factors? Explain your answer.
    b. What is the smallest the number could be?

12. Chairs for a meeting are arranged in six rows. Every row has the same number of chairs.
    a. What is the minimum possible number of chairs that could be in the room?
    b. If 100 is the maximum number of people allowed in the meeting room, what other numbers of chairs are possible?

13. Gloomy Toothpaste comes in two sizes: 9 ounces for $0.89 and 12 ounces for $1.15.
    a. Ben and Aaron bought the same amount of toothpaste. Ben bought only 9-ounce tubes, and Aaron bought only 12-ounce tubes. What is the smallest possible number of tubes each boy bought? (Hint: Use your knowledge of multiples to help you.)
    b. Which size tube is the better buy?

14. Circle the letter(s) of the statements that are always true about any prime number.
    a. It is divisible by only itself and 1.
    b. It is a factor of 1.
    c. It is divisible by another prime number.
    d. It is always an odd number.

15. Tyrone claims that the longest string of factors for 48 is $48 = 2 \times 2 \times 2 \times 2 \times 3$. Ian says there is a longer string. He wrote $48 = 1 \times 1 \times 1 \times 1 \times 1 \times 2 \times 2 \times 2 \times 2 \times 3$. Who is correct? Why?

16. What is the smallest number divisible by the first three prime numbers and the first three composite numbers? Explain how you got your answer.

Name _____ Date _____

1. Find three different ways to factor each of the following numbers into a product of factors. Do not use 1 as a factor.

   a. 72   b. 16

   c. 105   d. 132

2. A two-digit number that is less than 81 has 26 and 6 as factors. Find the number and explain your reasoning.

3. Fran has made a rectangle using 36 square tiles. The sum of the length and width of her rectangle is 15.

   a. What are the length and width of Fran's rectangle? Explain your reasoning.

   b. Would it be possible for the length and width of Fran's rectangle to be 11 and 4? Explain why or why not.

4. The diagrams below show three rectangles made from square tiles. Use the diagrams to answer each of the following questions.

   a. For each of the three rectangles, explain how the length and width of the rectangle are factors of the area of the rectangle.

   b. For each of the three rectangles, are the length and width the only factors of the area of the rectangle if you exclude a length or width of 1? Explain why or why not.

Unit Test

5. List all of the factor pairs for each of the following numbers.

    a. 48　　　　　　　　**b.** 93　　　　　　　　**c.** 32　　　　　　　　**d.** 102

6. Find the dimensions of all of the rectangles that can be made with the same number of tiles as in the rectangle below. Explain how you found your answers.

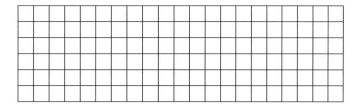

7. What number has the prime factorization $2^2 \times 3 \times 5^2 \times 7$? Explain your reasoning.

8. A number can be factored into the product $3^2 \times 9^3 \times 7^4$.

    a. Is the number even or odd? Explain your reasoning.

    b. Is the expression above the prime factorization of the number? Explain why or why not.

9. Marcia has developed a rule for generating a number sequence. The first 6 numbers in her sequence are 7, 21, 42, 126, 252, 756.

    a. What is Marcia's rule for finding the numbers in her sequence? Explain how you found your answer.

    b. What are the next two numbers in Marcia's sequence?

    c. What is the greatest common factor (GCF) of all the terms in Marcia's sequence? Explain your reasoning.

Notebook Checklist

Journal Organization

_____ Problems and Mathematical Reflections are labeled and dated.

_____ Work is neat and easy to find and follow.

Vocabulary

_____ All words are listed.   _____ All words are defined and described.

Quizzes and Check-Ups

_____ Quiz A   _____ Check-Up 1

_____ Quiz B   _____ Check-Up 2

Homework Assignments

_____ _____

_____ _____

_____ _____

_____ _____

_____ _____

_____ _____

_____ _____

_____ _____

_____ _____

_____ _____

_____ _____

_____ _____

_____ _____

_____ _____

_____ _____

_____ _____

Self-Assessment

Vocabulary

Of the vocabulary words I defined or described in my journal, the word _____ best demonstrates my ability to give a clear definition or description.

Of the vocabulary words I defined or described in my journal, the word _____ best demonstrates my ability to use an example to help explain or describe an idea.

Mathematical Ideas

1. **a.** I learned these things about numbers and their properties from *Prime Time*:

    b. Here are page numbers of journal entries that give evidence of what I have learned, along with descriptions of what each entry shows:

2. **a.** These are the mathematical ideas I am still struggling with:

    b. This is why I think these ideas are difficult for me:

    c. Here are page numbers of journal entries that give evidence of what I am struggling with, along with descriptions of what each entry shows:

Class Participation

I contributed to the classroom discussion and understanding of *Prime Time* when I…
(Give examples.)

© Dale Seymour Publications®

Answer Keys

Answers to Check-Up 1

1. 1, 5, 7, 35

2. 1, 2, 3, 6, 9, 18, 27, 54

3. 1, 2, 3, 6, 7, 14, 21

4. 1

5. 47

6. 35, 42, 54

7. 42, 54

8. odd; You can use tile models for odd and even numbers. If you combine a rectangle of height 2 (an even number) with a rectangle of height 2 with an extra tile (an odd number), you get a rectangle with an extra tile (an odd number).

Answers to Quiz A

1. The best move is 25, which gives your opponent only 5 points. Note: A prime number would be a bad move, since its only proper factor, 1, would already have been circled.

2. Possible response: We played the Factor Game today. I discovered that it is best to go first and choose 29, the highest prime on the board, as your first move. After the first move, choose numbers like 25 that leave your opponent a small number of factors. Stay away from numbers like 30, which have many factors, until most of the factors are already circled.

3. **a.** 2, 3, 4, 6, 8, 9

   b. 81

4. **a.** If we consider an $a \times b$ rectangle to be different from a $b \times a$ rectangle, 48 gives ten choices of rectangles.

   b. 36 and 49

Answers to Check-Up 2

1. 1 and 18, 2 and 9, 3 and 6

2. 1 and 25, 5 and 5

3. 1 and 36, 2 and 18, 3 and 12, 4 and 9, 6 and 6

4. 1 and 48, 2 and 24, 3 and 16, 4 and 12, 6 and 8

5. 1, 2, 3, 4, 6, 12

6. 1

7. 18, 36, 54, 72, 90, 108, 126, 144, 162, 180

8. 25, 50, 75, 100, 125, 150, 175, 200, 225, 250

9. 36, 72, 108, 144, 180, 216, 252, 288, 324, 360

10. 48, 96, 144, 192, 240, 288, 336, 384, 432, 480

11. 144 and 288

12. Possible answer: 432 and 1728

13. $2 \times 2 \times 2 \times 2 \times 3$

14. 5×19

15. $2 \times 2 \times 2 \times 3 \times 5$

16. Jill is incorrect. For 6 to be a common factor, both numbers must be divisible by 6. The number 56 cannot be divided evenly by 6.

Answers to Quiz B

1. a. 1 bag of 36 cookies, 2 bags of 18 cookies, 3 bags of 12 cookies, 4 bags of 9 cookies, 6 bags of 6 cookies, 9 bags of 4 cookies, 12 bags of 3 cookies, 18 bags of 2 cookies, 36 bags of 1 cookie

b. Possible answer: Two cookies in a bag would be affordable and is a number a student would typically eat. This would also allow more students to buy cookies.

c. Possible answer: Each cookie cost 15 cents to make. They could be sold at 25 cents per cookie. So, a bag of one would cost 25 cents, a bag of two would cost 50 cents, ...

2. a. in 72 minutes, or at 4:12 P.M.

b. at 9:00 P.M.

3. Any two numbers with no common factors will work. Examples are 7 and 4, 13 and 19, 6 and 25, 14 and 9

4. Any two numbers that share a common factor will work. Examples are 15 and 9, 10 and 25, 18 and 48, 45 and 81

5. If the numbers do not have a common factor, their least common multiple will be equal to their product. If the numbers have a common factor, their least common multiple will be less than their product.

6. Judith could have 1, 2, 3, 4, 6, or 12 children at the party. These numbers are the common factors of 24 and 36.

Answers to Question Bank

1. yes; The factors of numbers greater than 16 on the Factor Game board are between 1 and 15, so any number greater than 16 would be an illegal move, because its factors are already circled.

2. Possible answer: It is an even number. It can be divided by 2 without a remainder.

3. Possible answer: It can be divided by 3 without a remainder.

4. Possible answers: It can be divided by 5 without a remainder. It ends in 0 or 5.

5. 6, 12, 18, 24, 30, 36, 42, 48, 54, 60, 66, 72, 78, 84, 90, 96; Possible answers: They can be divided by 6 without a remainder. They have 6 as a factor. They are divisible by 2 and 3.

6. a. 225; To find all the factors of a number, you must check every whole number less than or equal to the square root of the number. If Mr. Matsumoto must check the numbers from 1 through 15, the number must be greater than or equal to 15 squared, or 225, and less than 16 squared, or 256.

b. 255; As mentioned in the answer to part a, the number must be less than 16 squared, or 256. The largest it could be is 255.

7. 11

8. Answers will vary.

9. **a.** 1, 4, 9, 16, 25, 36, 49, 64, 81, 100

    b.

Number	Factors
1	1
4	1, 2, 4
9	1, 3, 9
16	1, 2, 4, 8, 16
25	1, 5, 25
36	1, 2, 3, 4, 6, 9, 12, 18, 36
49	1, 7, 49
64	1, 2, 4, 8, 16, 32, 64
81	1, 3, 9, 27, 81
100	1, 2, 4, 5, 10, 20, 25, 50, 100

    c. 4, 9, 25, 49 (the squares of primes)

    d. 121

10. 81

11. **a.** 1, 2, 10, 20; If a number has 4 and 5 as factors, it must have the factors of 4 and 5 as factors, namely 1, 2, 4, and 5. It must also have the products of 2 and 5 and of 4 and 5 as factors, since these pairs of factors do not have any common factors.

    b. The smallest number is 20, because 4 and 5 do not have any common factors.

12. **a.** 6

    b. 12, 18, 24, 30, 36, 42, 48, 54, 60, 66, 72, 78, 84, 90, and 96

13. **a.** Ben bought four 9-ounce tubes. Aaron bought three 12-ounce tubes.

    b. The 12-ounce tube is the better buy at 9.6 cents per ounce. The 9-ounce tube cost 9.9 cents per ounce.

14. a

15. Both are correct, but Tyrone's is the accepted form. When we make a factor string, we use only prime factors. Otherwise, the strings could go on forever.

16. 120; The first three prime numbers are 2, 3, and 5. The first three composite numbers are $4 = 2 \times 2$, $6 = 2 \times 3$, and $8 = 2 \times 2 \times 2$. The shortest string that contains the factors of all these numbers is $2 \times 2 \times 2 \times 3 \times 5$. The smallest number that is divisible by all the numbers is the product of this string, which is 120.

Answers to Unit Test

1. For each of the numbers, other factorizations may be possible:

   a. $2 \times 36, 3 \times 24, 6 \times 12$ **b.** $2 \times 8, 4 \times 4, 2 \times 2 \times 4$

   c. $3 \times 35, 3 \times 5 \times 7, 15 \times 7$ **d.** $2 \times 66, 3 \times 44, 11 \times 12$

2. The number is $78 = 2 \times 3 \times 13 = 6 \times 13 = 3 \times 26$.

3. **a.** Fran has a 3×12 rectangle; $A = 3 \times 12 = 36$ square units, and
   $L + W = 3 + 12 = 15$ units.

   b. No, since the area of the rectangle would be $4 \times 11 = 44$ square units, *not* 36.

4. **a.** $2 \times 4 = 8, 2 \times 6 = 12, 3 \times 6 = 18$

   b. The 2×4 rectangle does not have any other possibilities since 8 has no other pair of
   proper factors. However, the other two rectangles do, i.e., $3 \times 4 = 12$ and $2 \times 9 = 18$.

5. **a.** $1 \times 48, 2 \times 24, 3 \times 16, 4 \times 12, 6 \times 8$ **b.** $1 \times 93, 3 \times 31$

   c. $1 \times 32, 2 \times 16, 4 \times 8$ **d.** $1 \times 102, 2 \times 51, 3 \times 34, 6 \times 17$

6. Students should list all of the factor pairs of 126 other than 6×21 which are the dimensions of the given rectangle:
   $1 \times 126, 2 \times 63, 3 \times 42, 7 \times 18, 9 \times 14$.

7. The number is the product of $4 \times 3 \times 25 \times 7 = 84 \times 25 = 2100$.

8. **a.** The number is odd since it does not have 2 as a factor.

   b. No, the factorization is not prime since it has 9 as a factor, and 9 is not prime. The actual
   prime factorization would be $3^8 \times 7^4$.

9. **a.** Alternate multiplying terms by 3 and 2 to generate the next term.

   b. 1512 and 4536

   c. 7, since it is the only prime number in the sequence and is a factor of all the other terms in the sequence no
   matter how many terms are added.

This section includes two samples of Product Game boards created by students in response to Problem 2.2. Each sample is followed by a teacher's comments about the board. These samples are included to give you an idea of what students have done for this problem and to help you think about how you might assess your students' work for instructional and reporting purposes.

Scoring rubric for Product Game boards

Determining factors	1 point
Finding and including all products	3 points
Board design and rules	2 points
Paragraph	2 points
Total:	8 points

Part of Problem 2.2 involves providing feedback about another group's game. A group receives 2 additional points if the game they checked includes all the necessary products and a complete set of rules.

Sample 1

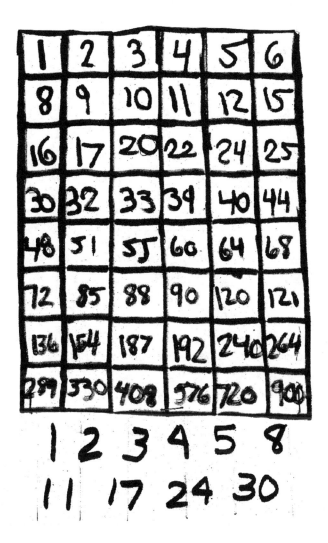

1	2	3	4	5	6
8	9	10	11	12	15
16	17	20	22	24	25
30	32	33	39	40	44
48	51	55	60	64	68
72	85	88	90	120	121
136	154	187	192	240	264
289	330	408	576	720	900

1 2 3 4 5 8

11 17 24 30

Products

1: 1
2: 2, 4
3: 3, 6, 9
4: 4, 8, 12, 16
5: 5, 10, 15, 20, 25
8: 8, 16, 24, 32, 40, 64
11: 11, 22, 33, 44, 55, 88, 121
17: 17, 34, 51, 68, 85, 136, 187, 289
24: 24, 49, 72, 96, 120, 192, 264, 408, 576
30: 30, 60, 90, 150, 240, 330, 510, 720, 900

We think are game is interesting because it has such high numbers to work with. We think it would be better to have to get only three in a row because it is very difficult to get four.

We had a big problem when we had to many numbers that didn't work with our game, so we had to draw the whole game board over and figure out the true numbers of the game.

A Teacher's Comments

Using the scoring rubric given above, this group would receive the following score:

Determining factors	1 points
Finding and including all products	2 points
Board design and rules	2 points
Paragraph	2 points
Total:	7 points

This group lost 1 point for "Finding and including all products" because their board did not include 96, 150, and 510, which are all possible products of factors on their list.

The group that gave this group feedback received only 1 of the 2 additional points because they did not point out that the board did not include all the possible products.

This group's work indicates that the task was appropriate. The students were able to carry out the project and show some understanding of the relationship between factors and products. The group used an effective scheme for organizing the products, and their circling system indicates an understanding that some products result from more than one pairing of factors. The missing products do not suggest that students are struggling with the ideas of factors and products, but rather that they did not fully understand the rules for creating the game.

Sample 2

The 10x10 Game

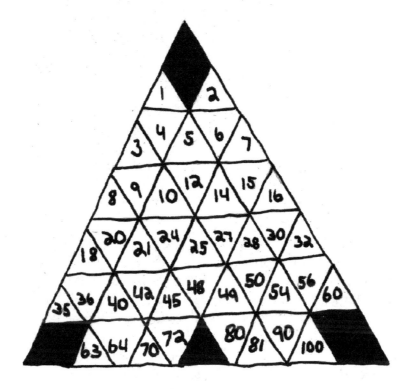

1 2 3 4 5 6 7 8 9 10

Factors	Products
1	1
2	2,4
3	3,6,9
4	8,12,16
5	5,10,15,20,25
6	18,24,30,36
7	7,14,21,28,35,42,49
8	32,40,48,56,64
9	27,45,54,63,72,81
10	50,60,70,80,90,100

We think our game board is interesting because it is a triangle. Some problems we ran into were we couldn't get the same amount of numbers as spaces so we marked spaces out

A Teacher's Comments

Using the scoring rubric given above, this group would receive the following score:

Determining factors	1 point
Finding and including all products	1 point
Board design and rules	1 point
Paragraph	2 points
Total:	5 points

This group received only 1 point for "Finding and including all products" because they simply repeated an example done in the Launch. During the Launch, the class generated all the products that would be needed if 10 were included as a factor. This group used this idea rather than creating a new game board. They received only 1 point for the "Board design and rules" because, although they showed creativity by making a triangular game board, they did not include a set of rules.

The group that gave this group feedback received no additional points because they did not remind this group to include a set of rules or point out that this was the same game created by the class.

This group shows some understanding of the relationship between factors and products. They did not list all the possible products in their chart, but, since the missing products are duplicates, the chart makes sense. The group lost points for using the same factors used during the Launch because I told the class not to simply reproduce what was done in class. The group providing feedback did not address this issue either. This suggests that I might want to rethink the way I launch the lesson. Next time I may write the directions on the board so that students can refer to them as they work on the problem.

The final assessment for *Prime Time* is the My Special Number Project. This project was introduced at the beginning of the student edition and formally assigned after Investigation 6. A possible scoring rubric and two sample projects with teacher comments are given here. The first sample is a report; the second is a story.

Suggested Scoring Rubric

This rubric for scoring the project employs a scale that runs from 0 to 4, with a 4+ for work that goes beyond what has been asked for in some unique way. You may use this rubric as presented here or modify it to fit your district's requirements for evaluating and reporting students' work and understanding.

4+ Exemplary Response
- Complete, with clear, coherent explanations
- Shows understanding of the mathematical concepts and procedures
- Satisfies all essential conditions of the problem and goes beyond what is asked for in some unique way

4 Complete Response
- Complete, with clear, coherent explanations
- Shows understanding of the mathematical concepts and procedures
- Satisfies all essential conditions of the problem

3 Reasonably Complete Response
- Reasonably complete; may lack detail in explanations
- Shows understanding of most of the mathematical concepts and procedures
- Satisfies most of the essential conditions of the problem

2 Partial Response
- Gives response; explanation may be unclear or lack detail
- Shows some understanding of some of the mathematical concepts and procedures
- Satisfies some essential conditions of the problem

1 Inadequate Response
- Incomplete; explanation is insufficient or not understandable
- Shows little understanding of the mathematical concepts and procedures
- Fails to address essential conditions of problem

0 No Attempt
- Irrelevant response
- Does not attempt a solution
- Does not address conditions of the problem

Sample 1

My Special Number

My special number is 71. I have always liked 71, because it is such an original number. I'll let you in on the mathematical terms for my special number, 71. For one thing, 71 is a prime number. A prime means that the number has only two factors. It is only divisible by one and itself. Since my number is a prime number, it absolutely is impossible for it to be a composite number. A composite number is a number that has more than two factors.

There are also some mathematical terms that you have probably heard of many times before. For instance, 71, is an odd number. That means that if the last number of a number has the numbers 1,3,5,7 or 9, than the number is odd. Since 71 is odd, than it can't be possibly be even. If

a number is even, it will have either a 0,2,4,6,8 at the end of the number.

Here are a little bit more facts about my number, 71. The factors of 71 are: 1 and 71. Factors are numbers that you can multiply with a number to equal another number. For instance, 71×1=71. 71 is a multiple of 1 and 71. A multiple is a number that increases by the same amount of numbers. It is also the answer to a multiplication problem. The only proper factor for 71 is 1. A proper factor is a number that is a factor of a number, but not the number itself.

Here are some facts about 71 that tell about the sum of it's factors. 71 is deficient. That means that the sum of it's proper factors add up to less than the number itself. Since 71 is deficient, it can't be abundant of perfect. If a

number is abundant, it means that the sum of the number's factors add up to more than the number itself. If the number is perfect, it means that the sum of the factors for that number equal up to the number itself.

Here are some facts about the shape of 71. 71 is a rectangle. That means that if you make a block or something that is 1×71, it will be a rectangle. Since 71 is a rectangle, that means that it is not a square. A square is if you make a block that is, let's say, 6×6, the figure will be a square.

Now I am going to tell you what 71 has in common with other numbers. Well for one thing, 71 does not have any common factors besides the obvious, 1 and 71. Common factors are factors that two or more numbers share. There common multiples of 2 and 71 are: 142,

284, and 426. Common multiples are multiples that two or more numbers share.

Here are some pretty long mathematical terms that most people are not very familiar with. First of all, the last digit of 71, one, has the identity property of 1. The identity property of one means, if you multiply any number by one, it will always equal the number that you started out with. Another long term is the Fundamental Theorem of Arithmetic. The Fundamental Theorem of Arithmetic is a system of multiplication, in which you multiply the factors of a number, in different orders, but always end up with the same product. Relatively Prime numbers are two numbers that can both share the common factor of 1, and only 1. For instance, 71 and 7 are relatively prime numbers,

because the only common factor they share is 1. A near perfect number is a number that is almost perfect. That means that the sum of the factors for the number are one or two numbers off from equaling the multiple. 71 is not a near perfect number. Prime Factorization is when you factor out a number down to only prime numbers. For instance a factor tree is an example of prime factorization. Below is the prime factorization of 71 on a factor tree.

$$71$$
$$\diagup\diagdown \leftarrow \text{factor tree}$$
$$1 \quad x \quad 71$$

A Teacher's Comments

From reading this report, I get a feeling about which ideas this student has made some sense of and some things with which she is still struggling.

The student has used all the listed vocabulary words for this unit and some additional terms *(Identity Property of 1* and *near-perfect number).* If I look at just the words identified as essential to this unit, she seems to have made good sense and usage of *factor, proper factor, common multiples, prime,* and *composite.* The terms not identified as essential—*abundant, deficient, perfect,* and *near-perfect number*—are used effectively. This conclusion can be drawn from the definitions the student has given and the ways she has used the words to explain her number. (Look at the paragraph on prime and composite numbers as an example of what I mean.)

Other words she has used, but less clearly or lacking in detail, are *multiples* (weak explanation), *prime factorization* (right definition, but her prime factorization includes 1, so I have to wonder whether she knows 1 is not prime), and *relatively prime* (right definition, yet she has chosen two prime numbers, so I'm not sure if she knows relatively prime numbers do not have to be prime themselves).

Another weakness of the paper is in her use of the terms *even* and *odd.* Her definition for these words is given as a rule, and she shows no evidence of understanding the mathematics of what it means to be an even or odd number. She also seems confused about the term *common factor.* Her definition is adequate—"factors that two or more numbers share"—but then says 71 does not have any common factors other than 1 and 71. She makes no reference to comparing 71 with another number to look for common factors.

The student shows lack of understanding of the Fundamental Theorem of Arithmetic. Her definition sounds more like a definition for the Commutative Property of Multiplication. There is no mention of the prime factorization of a number.

The part of the paper that leaves me very confused is where she claims "71 is a rectangle" and "since 71 is a rectangle, that means that it is not a square." Part of me wonders whether she is trying to make sense of square numbers, and part of me wonders whether having students build rectangles from a certain number of tiles and on grid paper has caused confusion between the ideas of factors of a number and rectangles.

Considering the paper as a whole, I believe this student shows she has made sense of the ideas in this unit. I am most concerned with her lack of evidence of understanding common multiples because of the importance of this concept. On a 4-point scale, I would give this student a 3.

Sample 2

"And for your homework," said Ms. Hukin, "You need to pick a number and show me the following mathematical things about it."

Bobby hated math homework about as much as he hated Ms. Hukin. Ms. Hukin was 62 and she always wore a sweater and long skirt, even when it was 92 outside and the school's air conditioning is broke-like today. Bobby also hated the way Ms. Hukin always looked at him, she had sharp piercing eyes. It almost felt as if she were trying to stab him with a glance.

Bobby couldn't believe that Ms. Hukin had given them such a huge assignment and only one day to do it in. How was he supposed to get it done? He didn't even understand the stupid thing. Plus his brother was out of town so he had no one to bribe to do it for him. HE WAS GOING TO HAVE TO DO THIS ONE ON HIS OWN!!

Bobby sat down at his desk in his desk in his room and opened

his binder to a blank sheet of paper. It was exactly 7:00. Bobby picked up his pencil and wrote, my number which is 14 is even cause it is. As Bobby was finishing the last word he heard a knock at the door...

When Bobby opened the door he saw a horrid figure stading before him. The figure spoke, "I am the ghost of math past." Bobby replied "OOOOOK." "You must come with me," the figure said. Bobby followed the figure into the hallway but as he stepped into the hallway Bobby realized it was no longer the hallway, instead he was standing in his 3rd grade classroom.

Bobby can you tell me why your number is even or odd?"Yes Ms. Shicken, my number which is 14 is even because it is devisable by 2," replied little Bobby, "very good now can you tell me why it is not odd" asked Ms. Shicken. "Yes Ms. Shicken it is not odd because it is devisable

by 2."

Bobby couldn't believe his eyes he just saw himself in the 3rd grade talking to his teacher. "We must go now, further in the past."

Bobby now found himself in his nursery. They were all the way back to when he was a baby. His parent's walked into the room. "Oh what a cute baby," said his mother. "That's my boy, now for your first math lesson my boy, 14 is a deficient number because all of it's factors added up equal less than itself. It is also of course not a perfect number because all of it's factors added up do not equal itself. Got that my boy."

"I always said my father was a little weird," Bobby said to the figure. "You must go back now," said the ghost of math past as he reached over and touched Bobby on the head. All of a sudden Bobby found himself in his own house in his own room. "Cool!" yelled Bobby.

KNOCK KNOCK

"Oh great here we go again!" As Bobby opened the door he saw yet another hideous creature standing before him. It spoke "I am the ghost of of math present, you must come with me." As Bobby stepped into the hallway he found himself standing in Ms. Hukin's room. Bobby looked around and found his desk but he was not sitting there, he must have been in bathroom. Everyone was chanting BOBBY SO STUPID HE DOESN'T EVEN KNOW WHAT A FACTOR IS. "Class settle down," yelled Ms. Hukin. Now Silvia tell me all the factors of 14." "O.K. 1,2, and 7," said Shirley. "O.K. and tell me the definition of a factor." "OK, factors are the numbers that will go evenly into a certain number." "Very good."

"Oh look here I come," Bobby said as he saw himself walk into the room. "AAAHH there you are Bobby now sit down and tell me what a multiple is," said Ms. Hukin. "Beats me!" "Oh let me answer!" screamed Shirley. "A multiple

---

is the sum of a certain number times a certain number, for example 14x2=28 so 28 is a multiple of 14." "Very good, start listening Bobby."

All of a sudden Bobby heard the ghost mumbling to himself "A common multiple is a multiple that 2 different numbers have for example 28 is a common multiple for 2 and 14." "What?" asked Bobby. "Oh sorry I'm studying for a math test," replied the figure.

Bobby blinked for one second and found himself back in his own room. There was a knock at the door.

As Bobby opened the door he saw, yeah you got it another hideous figure. It did not look at Bobby it kept it's head down looking at a paper "4 is a composite number because it has more than one and itself as a factor that is the same reason it's not a prime number, an example of a prime number is 17 it's prime because it's

---

only factors are 1 and itself. "Math test, huh?" asked Bobby. "Yeah oh wait a second here. I am the ghost of math future." "Save it. Listen I want to help you out with your math test, I mean your buddies have been so good to me I figure hay why not." "Great, listen what I don't get is prime factorization." "Oh that's simple, prime factorization is a number broken down into its prime factors for example 14. 14 isn't prime because 7x2=14. 7 and 2 are both prime so thats 14's prime factorization."

All of a sudden the ghost disappeared and Bobby heard his mother calling him. He was back in his desk with the sheet of paper in front of him. He was surprised though because he actually knew what everything ment.

A Teacher's Comments

This piece is very clever with its unique takeoff on *A Christmas Carol*. Yet, what I am most interested in, as a mathematics teacher, is what this student demonstrates about his understanding of the mathematical ideas from this unit.

This student has addressed fewer vocabulary words than the student in the first paper. What is most important is what he says and how he used the words that have been identified as essential. Considering those words first, he seems to have made good sense of *common multiple, factor, prime factorization,* and *prime* and *composite number.* He also has effectively used the words *abundant, deficient, perfect, odd,* and *even numbers.* This conclusion is made from the definition he has given and the ways he used the words in his story. (Look at the paragraph on composite and prime numbers as an example of what I mean.)

The student struggles with the word *multiple.* His example is reasonable, but his definition is confusing. I am not sure what he means when he says, "A multiple is the sum of a certain number times a certain number."

What weakens this paper is the fact that the student did not address two of the essential words from the vocabulary list. There is no evidence of what sense he has made of the ideas of *common factor* and *proper factor.* Because common factor is such an important mathematical idea, I would want to make sure I addressed this with the student.

Considering the paper as a whole, I believe this student shows he has made lots of sense of the ideas in this unit. On a 4-point scale, I would give this student a 3 because of a lack of completeness in not addressing common and proper factors and the weak description of multiples. I believe that if this student were given a chance to revise this paper, with little prompting the paper could easily become a 4.

Blackline Masters

Factor Game Boards

The Factor Game

1	2	3	4	5
6	7	8	9	10
11	12	13	14	15
16	17	18	19	20
21	22	23	24	25
26	27	28	29	30

The Factor Game

1	2	3	4	5
6	7	8	9	10
11	12	13	14	15
16	17	18	19	20
21	22	23	24	25
26	27	28	29	30

The Factor Game

1	2	3	4	5
6	7	8	9	10
11	12	13	14	15
16	17	18	19	20
21	22	23	24	25
26	27	28	29	30

The Factor Game

1	2	3	4	5
6	7	8	9	10
11	12	13	14	15
16	17	18	19	20
21	22	23	24	25
26	27	28	29	30

Table for Recording First Moves

Possible first move	Proper factors	My score	Opponent's score
1			
2			
3			
4			
5			
6			
7			
8			
9			
10			
11			
12			
13			
14			
15			
16			
17			
18			
19			
20			
21			
22			
23			
24			
25			
26			
27			
28			
29			
30			

Product Game Boards

The Product Game

1	2	3	4	5	6
7	8	9	10	12	14
15	16	18	20	21	24
25	27	28	30	32	35
36	40	42	45	48	49
54	56	63	64	72	81

Factors:
  1 2 3 4 5 6 7 8 9

The Product Game

1	2	3	4	5	6
7	8	9	10	12	14
15	16	18	20	21	24
25	27	28	30	32	35
36	40	42	45	48	49
54	56	63	64	72	81

Factors:
  1 2 3 4 5 6 7 8 9

The Product Game

1	2	3	4	5	6
7	8	9	10	12	14
15	16	18	20	21	24
25	27	28	30	32	35
36	40	42	45	48	49
54	56	63	64	72	81

Factors:
  1 2 3 4 5 6 7 8 9

The Product Game

1	2	3	4	5	6
7	8	9	10	12	14
15	16	18	20	21	24
25	27	28	30	32	35
36	40	42	45	48	49
54	56	63	64	72	81

Factors:
  1 2 3 4 5 6 7 8 9

The Product Puzzle

The Product Puzzle

30	×	14	×	8	×	7	×	210	×
×	2	×	4	×	3	×	2	×	2
105	×	2	×	5	×	84	×	56	×
×	21	×	2	×	7	×	8	×	3
40	×	20	×	4	×	7	×	5	×
×	4	×	28	×	5	×	3	×	2
6	×	8	×	21	×	2	×	105	×
×	2	×	10	×	2	×	5	×	2
32	×	3	×	14	×	60	×	56	×
×	5	×	8	×	15	×	7	×	3

Strings Found in the Product Puzzle

105 × 2 × 4

_____

_____

_____

_____

_____

_____

_____

_____

_____

_____

Play the Factor Game several times with a partner. Take turns making the first move. Look for moves that give the best scores. In your journal, record any strategies you find that help you to win.

The Factor Game

1	2	3	4	5
6	7	8	9	10
11	12	13	14	15
16	17	18	19	20
21	22	23	24	25
26	27	28	29	30

Possible first move	Proper factors	My score	Opponent's score
1	None	Lose a turn	0
2	1	2	1
3	1	3	1
4	1, 2	4	3
5			
6			
7			
8			
9			
10			
11			
12			
13			
14			
15			
16			
17			
18			
19			
20			
21			
22			
23			
24			
25			
26			
27			
28			
29			
30			

Use your list to figure out the best and worst first moves.

A. What is the best first move? Why?

B. What is the worst first move? Why?

C. Look for other patterns in your list. Describe an interesting pattern that you find.

Play the Product Game several times with a partner. Look for interesting patterns and winning strategies. Make notes of your observations.

The Product Game

1	2	3	4	5	6
7	8	9	10	12	14
15	16	18	20	21	24
25	27	28	30	32	35
36	40	42	45	48	49
54	56	63	64	72	81

Factors:
1 2 3 4 5 6 7 8 9

Work with your partner to design a new game board for the Product Game.

■ Choose factors to include in your factor list.

■ Determine the products you need to include on the game board.

■ Find a game board that will accommodate all the products.

■ Decide how many squares a player must get in a row—up and down, across, or diagonally—to win.

Make the game board. Play your game against your partner; then make any changes you both agree would make your game more interesting.

Switch game boards with another pair, and play their game. Give them some written suggestions about how they can improve their game. Read the suggestions for improving your game, then make any changes you and your partner think are necessary.

Copy the Venn diagram below.

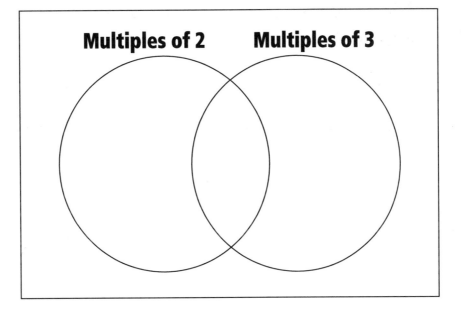

Find at least five numbers that belong in each region of the
diagram. Think about what numbers belong in the intersection
of the circles and what numbers belong outside of the circles.

Terrapin Crafts wants to rent a space of 12 square yards.

A. Use 12 square tiles to represent the 12 square yards. Find all the possible ways the Terrapin Crafts owner can arrange the squares. Copy each rectangle you make onto grid paper, and label it with its dimensions (length and width).

B. How are the rectangles you found and the factors of 12 related?

Suppose Terrapin Crafts decided it wanted a space of 16 square yards.

C. Find all the possible ways the Terrapin Crafts owner can arrange the 16 square yards. Copy each rectangle you make onto grid paper, and label it with its dimensions.

D. How are these rectangles and the factors of 16 related?

Work with your group to decide how to divide up the numbers you have been assigned.

Cut out a grid-paper model of each rectangle you can make for each of the numbers you have been assigned. You may want to use tiles to help you find the rectangles.

Write each number at the top of a sheet of paper, and tape all the rectangles for that number to the sheet. Display the sheets of rectangles in order from 1 to 30 around the room.

When all the numbers are displayed, look for patterns. Be prepared to discuss patterns you find with your classmates.

Make a conjecture about whether each result below will be even or odd. Then use tile models or some other method to justify your conjecture.

A. The sum of two even numbers

B. The sum of two odd numbers

C. The sum of an odd number and an even number

D. The product of two even numbers

E. The product of two odd numbers

F. The product of an odd number and an even number

You and your little sister go to a carnival that has both a large and a small Ferris wheel. You get on the large Ferris wheel at the same time your sister gets on the small Ferris wheel. The rides begin as soon as you are both buckled into your seats. Determine the number of seconds that will pass before you and your sister are both at the bottom again

A. if the large wheel makes one revolution in 60 seconds and the small wheel makes one revolution in 20 seconds.

B. if the large wheel makes one revolution in 50 seconds and the small wheel makes one revolution in 30 seconds.

C. if the large wheel makes one revolution in 10 seconds and the small wheel makes one revolution in 7 seconds.

Stephan's grandfather told him about a terrible year when the cicadas were so numerous that they ate all the crops on his farm. Stephan conjectured that both 13-year and 17-year locusts came out that year. Assume Stephan's conjecture is correct.

A. How many years pass between the years when both 13-year and 17-year locusts are out at the same time? Explain how you got your answer.

B. Suppose there were 12-year, 14-year, and 16-year locusts, and they all came out this year. How many years will it be before they all come out together again? Explain how you got your answer.

Miriam's uncle donated 120 cans of juice and 90 packs of cheese crackers for the school picnic. Each student is to receive the same number of cans of juice and the same number of packs of crackers.

What is the largest number of students that can come to the picnic and share the food equally? How many cans of juice and how many packs of crackers will each student receive? Explain how you got your answers.

In the Product Puzzle, find as many factor strings for 840 as you can. A string can go around corners as long as there is a multiplication sign, ×, between any two numbers. When you find a string, draw a loop around it. Keep a record of the strings you find.

The Product Puzzle

30	×	14	×	8	×	7	×	210	×
×	2	×	4	×	3	×	2	×	2
105	×	2	×	5	×	84	×	56	×
×	21	×	2	×	7	×	8	×	3
40	×	20	×	4	×	7	×	5	×
×	4	×	28	×	5	×	3	×	2
6	×	8	×	21	×	2	×	105	×
×	2	×	10	×	2	×	5	×	2
32	×	3	×	14	×	60	×	56	×
×	5	×	8	×	15	×	7	×	3

Strings Found in the Product Puzzle

105 × 2 × 4

_____

_____

_____

_____

_____

_____

_____

_____

_____

_____

Work with a partner to find the longest factorization for 600. You may make a factor tree or use another method. When you are finished, compare your results with the results of your classmates.

Did everyone produce the same results? If so, what was is the longest factorization for 600? If not, what differences occurred?

A. Try using Heidi's methods to find the greatest common factor and least common multiple of 48 and 72 and of 30 and 54.

B. Are Heidi's methods correct? Explain your thinking. If you think Heidi is wrong, revise her methods so they are correct.

When the students are finished, which locker doors are open?

Dear Family,

The first unit in your child's course of study in mathematics class this year is *Prime Time.* Its focus is whole numbers, and it teaches students about factors, multiples, divisors, products, prime numbers, composite numbers, common factors and multiples, and many other ideas about numbers. This unit engages students in a series of activities that allow them to discover many of the key properties of numbers and to see how these properties apply to real-life situations.

As part of the assessment for this unit, your child will be asked to do a project called "My Special Number." The project is introduced at the beginning of the unit, when each student is asked to choose a special number and write several things about it. As students work throught the unit, they apply what they have learned to write new information about their numbers. At the end of the unit, students create projects which include everything they have learned about their numbers.

You can help your child in several ways:

- Have your child share his or her mathematics notebook with you, showing you what has been recorded about numbers. Ask your child to explain why these ideas are important.

- Have your child show you the boards for playing the Factor Game and the Product Game. Ask your child to explain the rules, and, if you have time, offer to play a game.

- Look over your child's homework and make sure all questions are answered and that explanations are clear.

As always, if you have any questions or concerns about this unit or your child's progress in the class, please feel free to call. All of us here are interested in your child and want to be sure that this year's mathematics experiences are enjoyable and promote a firm understanding of mathematics.

Sincerely,

Estimada familia,

La primera unidad del programa de matemáticas de su hijo o hija para este curso se llama *Prime Time (Primero los primos)*. La misma trata principalmente sobre los números enteros; en ella los alumnos estudiarán los factores, los múltiplos; los divisores, los productos, los números primos, los números compuestos, los factores y los múltiplos comunes y otros mucho conceptos numéricos. Realizarán también una serie de actividades clave de los números y observar cómo éstas se aplican a situaciones de la vida real.

Como parte de la evaluación de esta unidad, a su hijo o hija se le pedirá un proyecto llamado "Mi número especial." Se expondrá el proyecto al principio de la unidad, momento en el cual cada alumno deberá escoger un número especial y escribir algunas de sus características. Durante el estudio de la unidad, los alumnos, basándose en los conocimientos que vayan adquiriendo, escribirán nuevas características de los números. Una vez terminada la unidad, hará proyectos que abarquen todo lo aprendido sobre esos números.

Ustedes pueden ayudar a su hijo o hija de las siguientes maneras:

- Pídanle que compara con ustedes al cuaderno de matemáticas, que les muestre sus anotaciones sobre los números y que les explique por qué éstas son importantes.

- Díganle que les enseñe los tableros, tanto el del Juego de los factores y como el del Juego de los productos, y que les explique las reglas de ambos. Y si ustedes disponen de tiempo libre, lo ideal sería que echasen una partida con su hijo o hija.

- Repasen le tarea de su hijo o hoja para asegurarse de que conteste todas las preguntas y escriba con claridad las explicaciones.

Y como de costumbre, si ustedes necesitan más detalles o aclaraciones respecto a esta unidad o sobre los progresos de su hijo o hija en esta clase, no duden llamarnos. A todas nos interesa su hijo o hija y queremos asegurarnos de que las experiencias matemáticas que tenga este año sean lo más amenas posibles y ayuden fomentar en él o ella una sólida comprensión de las matemáticas.

Atentamente,

Grid Paper

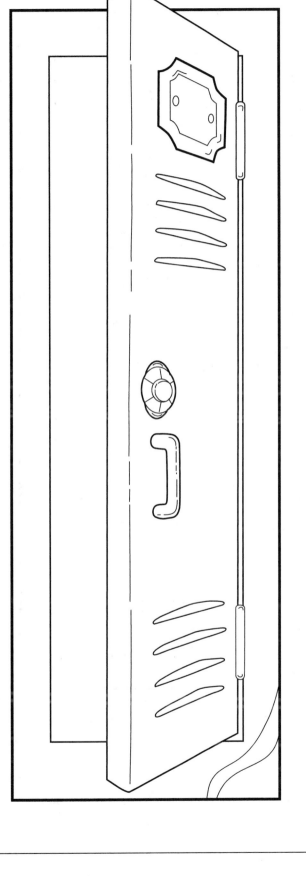

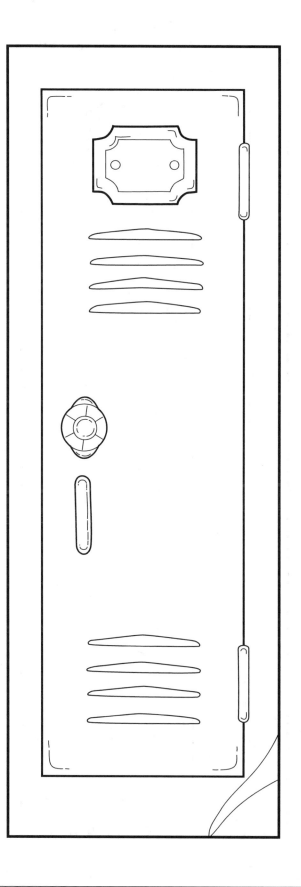

Additional Practice

Investigation 1

1. For each of the following, use the set of clues to determine the secret number.

   a. **Clue 1** The number has two digits.

       Clue 2 The number has 13 as a factor.

       Clue 3 The sum of the digits of the number is 11.

   b. **Clue 1** The number is prime.

       Clue 2 The number is less than 19.

       Clue 3 The sum of the digits of the number is greater than 7.

   c. **Clue 1** The number has three digits.

       Clue 2 The number is less than 140.

       Clue 3 The number has 7 as a factor.

       Clue 4 The number is even.

       Clue 5 The sum of the digits of the number is less than 9.

2. The numbers 10, 20, and 30 all have 5 and 10 as factors. Does *any* number that has 10 as a factor also have 5 as a factor? Explain your reasoning.

3. The numbers 14, 28, and 42 all have 2 and 7 as factors. Does *any* number that has 7 as a factor also have 2 as a factor? Explain your reasoning.

4. Suppose you are playing the Factor Game using a 100-board (that is, using a board with the numbers from 1 to 100).

   a. Suppose you circle 97 on the first move of the game.

       i. List all the factors of 97.

       ii. Determine the number of points you receive for the move.

   b. Suppose you circle 98 on the first move of the game.

       i. List all the factors of 98.

       ii. Determine the number of points your opponent receives for the move.

   c. Which is the better first move on the 100-board, 97 or 98? Explain your reasoning.

5. Find the two numbers on the 30-board with the greatest product.

   a. What two numbers did you pick? What is the product of the two numbers?

   b. Explain why the product of the two numbers is the greatest possible product.

   c. List all the proper factors of the product, and explain how you found the factors.

Investigation 2

1. For each of the following, find three different numbers that you could multiply to get the given product. Do not use 1 as one of the numbers.

   a. 150

   b. 1000

   c. 24

   d. 66

2. Ms. O'Brian's math class has developed a secret code. Each letter of the alphabet is assigned a multiple of 4, starting with 4 and ending with 104, so A = 4, B = 8, C = 12, and so on, up to Y = 100 and Z = 104. To code a message, the letters in each word are replaced with the corresponding code number and separated with dashes. For example, the code for the word MATH would be 52-4-80-32. To decode the message, each number is matched to its corresponding letter. In this case, 52 = M, 4 = A, 80 = T, and 32 = H.

   a. Make a table showing the code number for each letter of the alphabet.

   b. Use your table to decode this message. Note that a gap indicates the start of the next word.

      16-60   100-60-84-72   32-60-52-20-92-60-72-44

   c. Write your first and last name in this secret code.

   d. What is the secret code for the word DAYTIME?

   e. A student in Ms. O'Brian's class noticed that all the code numbers are even. Explain why this is true.

3. A particular three-digit number is less than 175 and has 4 and 11 as factors. What is the number?

4. The number sequence 4, 6, 10 is a multiple of the sequence 2, 3, 5 because 4, 6, 10 can be found by multiplying each number in the sequence 2, 3, 5 by 2. That is, $4 = 2 \times 2$, $6 = 2 \times 3$, $10 = 2 \times 5$.

   a. The number sequence 15, 25, 10 is a multiple of what number sequence?

   b. Find two sequences that are multiples of the sequence 1, 4, 7.

   c. How many multiples does a given number sequence have? Explain your reasoning.

5. Write as many different multiplication and division statements as you can using the given set of numbers. For example, if the numbers are 5, 7, 35, you can write:

      $5 \times 7 = 35$ $7 \times 5 = 35$ $35 \div 5 = 7$ $35 \div 7 = 5$

   a. 6, 4, 24

   b. 96, 12, 8, 3, 32

   c. 6, 27, 108, 12, 4, 18, 9

Investigation 3

1. Alicia has made a rectangle using 24 square tiles. If she adds the length and width of her rectangle together, she gets 11. What are the length and width of Alicia's rectangle? Explain your reasoning.

2. Jennifer has made a rectangle from 48 square tiles. If she adds the length and width of her rectangle together, she gets a prime number. What are the length and width of Jennifer's rectangle? Explain your reasoning.

3. List all the factor pairs for each of the following numbers.

    a. 56   b. 42   c. 31

    d. 80   e. 75   f. 108

    g. 225   h. 48   i. 49

4. Phillip is thinking of a number that is less than 20 and has three factor pairs. Phillip says that if he adds the factors in each factor pair, he gets 19, 11, and 9. What is Phillip's number? Explain how you found your answer.

5. Sketch all the rectangles that can be made with 36 square tiles. Use your rectangles to write down all the factor pairs of 36.

6. In each of the rectangles below, only the tiles along the length and width are shown. For each rectangle, tell how many square tiles it would take to make the rectangle.

    a. 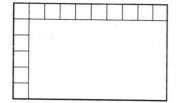   b. 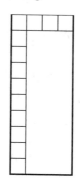   c.

7. You can model an even number with a rectangle made of two identical rows of tiles. So, 10 would be 2 rows of 5 tiles. You can model an odd number with two rows of tiles in which one row has one more tile than the other row. For example, 11 would be a row of 5 tiles and a row of 6 tiles. Use this idea to help you make and justify conjectures about whether each result will be odd or even.

    a. an even number times an even number

    b. an even number times an odd number

    c. an odd number times an odd number

Investigation 4

1. On Saturdays, the #14 bus makes roundtrips between Susan's school and the mall, and the #11 bus makes roundtrips between the mall and the museum. Next Saturday, Susan wants to take the bus from her school to the museum. A #14 bus leaves Susan's school every 15 minutes, beginning at 7 A.M. It takes the bus 30 minutes to travel between school and the mall. A #11 bus leaves the mall every 12 minutes beginning at 7 A.M.

   a. If Susan gets on the #14 bus at 9:30 A.M., how long will she have to wait at the mall for a #11 bus? Explain your reasoning.

   b. If Susan gets on the #11 bus at the museum and arrives at the mall at 11:48 A.M., how long will she have to wait for the #14 bus? Explain your reasoning.

   c. At what times between 9 A.M. and noon are the #14 and #11 buses at the mall at the same time? Explain your reasoning.

2. Kyong has built two rectangles with different areas. Each rectangle has a width of 7 tiles. Each rectangle is made with an even number of tiles that is greater than 40 but less than 60.

   a. How many tiles are in each rectangle? Explain your reasoning.

   b. What is the length of each of Kyong's rectangles? Explain your reasoning.

   c. Kyong rearranges the tiles of the rectangles to form different rectangles. What lengths and widths are possible for Kyong's new rectangles? Explain your reasoning.

3. Jack plays on a basketball team every third day of each month. He babysits his younger brother every seventh day of each month. How many times during a 30-day month will Jack have a conflict between basketball and babysitting? Explain your reasoning.

4. If two numbers are both prime, what is the least common multiple of the numbers? Explain your reasoning.

5. If two numbers have no common factors other than 1, they are said to be *relatively prime*. For example, the numbers 9 and 14 are relatively prime.

   a. Are 45 and 64 relatively prime? Explain your reasoning.

   b. Are 25 and 36 relatively prime? Explain your reasoning.

   c. Are 34 and 51 relatively prime? Explain your reasoning.

   d. Is it possible for two even numbers to be relatively prime? Why or why not?

6. Find the least common multiple and the greatest common factor for each pair of numbers:

   a. 8 and 12   b. 7 and 15   c. 11 and 17   d. 36 and 108

   e. For which pairs in parts a–d is the least common multiple the product of the two numbers? Why is this so?

Investigation 5

1. Find the prime factorization for each of the numbers below.

   a. 630   b. 144   c. 101   d. 133

2. Solve each multiplication maze below.

   a.
   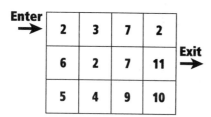

   b.
   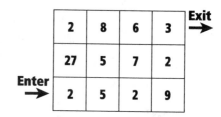

   c.
   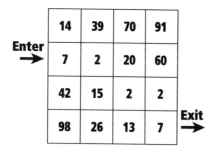

   d.
   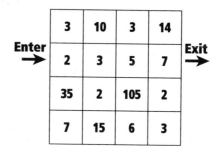

3. For each pair of numbers below, find the greatest common factor and the least common multiple.

   a. 25 and 105   b. 27 and 81   c. 36 and 63

4. An odd number is less than 160 and has exactly three different prime factors. What is the number? Explain your reasoning.

5. a. Name a pair of numbers whose greatest common factor is one of the numbers in the pair.

   b. Name another pair of numbers whose greatest common factor is one of the numbers in the pair.

   c. Make a conjecture about what must be true about the least common multiple of any number pair for which the greatest common factor is one of the numbers in the pair.

Investigation 6

1. Find all the numbers less than 500 that have 3 as their only prime factor. Explain your strategy for finding all of these numbers.

2. A *number sequence* is an ordered set of numbers that follows a pattern or rule. Jason has developed a rule for generating a number sequence. The first five numbers in his sequence are 3, 15, 30, 150, 300, and 1500.

   a. What is Jason's rule for finding the numbers in his sequence? Explain how you found your answer.

   b. What are the next two numbers in Jason's sequence?

   c. What will always be the greatest common factor of all the numbers in Jason's sequence, no matter how many new numbers he adds to the sequence? Explain your reasoning.

3. A set of consecutive numbers that contains no prime numbers is called a *prime desert*. For example, the set {14, 15, 16} is a prime desert because it is a set of consecutive numbers in which none of the numbers are prime. Find the largest prime desert (that is, the prime desert with the most numbers) in which all the numbers are less than 50.

4. For each of the sets of clues below, find the secret number.

   a. **Clue 1**　The number is less than 130.

   　　Clue 2　The number ends in a 5.

   　　Clue 3　The number is a multiple of a prime that is greater than 20 but less than 30.

   b. **Clue 1**　The number ends in a 0.

   　　Clue 2　The number is a multiple of 21.

   　　Clue 3　The number is less than 400.

5. Find the prime factorization of each of the following numbers.

   a. 190　　　　　　b. 319　　　　　　c. 255　　　　　　d. 406

Answer Keys

Investigation 1

1. a. 65   **b.** 17   **c.** 112

2. yes; Since 2 and 5 are factors of 10, any number that has 10 as a factor must also have 5 as a factor.

3. no; For example, the number 35 has 7 as a factor, but since it is an odd number it does not have 2 as a factor.

4. a. i. The only factors of 97 are 1 and 97.   **ii.** 97

   b. i. 1, 2, 7, 14, 49   **ii.** 73

   c. 97 is the better first move because you get 97 points, and your opponent gets only 1 point. If you choose 98 first, you get 98 points, but your opponent gets 73.

5. a. 29 and 30, which have a product of $29 \times 30 = 870$

   b. These two numbers give the largest product because they are the largest numbers.

   c. 1, 2, 3, 5, 6, 10, 15, 29, 30, 58, 87, 145, 174, 290, 435

Investigation 2

1. Students' answers will vary, but the following are examples of correct answers:

   a. $2 \times 5 \times 15$ **b.** $4 \times 10 \times 25$ **c.** $2 \times 3 \times 4$ **d.** $2 \times 3 \times 11$

2. a. Students will vary in how they organize their tables, but each letter should be shown with its corresponding number.

   b. DO YOUR HOMEWORK

   c. Answers will vary.

   d. 16-4-100-80-36-52-20

   e. yes; The code numbers will always be even because each code number is a multiple of 4, which is a multiple of 2.

3. 132

4. a. 3, 5, 2   **b.** Possible answer: 2, 8, 14 and 3, 12, 21   **c.** infinitely many

5. a. $6 \times 4 = 24$; $4 \times 6 = 24$; $24 \div 6 = 4$; $24 \div 4 = 6$

   b. $8 \times 12 = 96$; $12 \times 8 = 96$; $96 \div 12 = 8$; $96 \div 8 = 12$; $3 \times 32 = 96$; $32 \times 3 = 96$; $96 \div 32 = 3$; $96 \div 3 = 32$

   c. $6 \times 18 = 108$; $18 \times 6 = 108$; $108 \div 6 = 18$; $108 \div 18 = 6$; $4 \times 27 = 108$; $27 \times 4 = 108$; $108 \div 4 = 27$; $108 \div 27 = 4$; $9 \times 12 = 108$; $12 \times 9 = 108$; $108 \div 9 = 12$; $108 \div 12 = 9$

Investigation 3

1. The dimensions are 3×8. The possible dimensions are 1×24, 2×12, 3×8, and 4×6. Only the 3×8 rectangle has dimensions with a sum of 11.

2. The dimensions are 3×16. The possible dimensions are 1×48, 2×24, 3×16, 4×12, and 6×8. Only the 3×16 rectangle has dimensions with a sum that is a prime number.

3. **a.** 1×56, 2×28, 4×14, 7×8.

    b. 1×42, 2×21, 3×14, 6×7.

    c. 1×31

    d. 1×80, 2×40, 4×20, 5×16, 8×10.

    e. 1×75, 3×25, 5×15

    f. 1×108, 2×54, 3×36, 4×22, 6×18, 9×12

    g. 1×225, 3×75, 5×45, 15×15

    h. 1×48, 2×24, 3×16, 4×12, 6×8

    i. 1×49, 7×7

4. Phillip's number is 18 since the factor pairs 1×18, 2×9, 3×6 have the required sums and $18 < 20$.

5. Students should sketch rectangles having the dimensions 1×36, 2×18, 3×12, 4×9, 6×6.

6. **a.** 60   **b.** 40   **c.** 40

7. **a.** You can combine any number of even-number rectangles to produce another rectangle.

    b. You can combine any two odd-number models to produce an even-number rectangle; therefore, an even number of odd models will give an even-number rectangle.

    c. An odd number of odd models always leaves the extra tile, so an odd number times an odd number will be odd.

Investigation 4

1. **a.** Susan shouldn't have to wait at all, the #14 bus should arrive at the mall at 10 A.M. and the #11 bus should leave the mall for the museum at about 10 A.M. (since the #11 bus runs every 12 minutes, it leaves at the top of every hour).

    b. Susan will have to wait 12 minutes because the #14 bus should arrive at noon.

    c. Both buses are at the mall at 9 A.M., 10 A.M., 11 A.M., and noon because the least common multiple of 15 and 12 is 60.

2. **a.** One rectangle is made with 42 tiles, and the other is made with 56 tiles. These are the only two even multiples of 7 between 40 and 60.

    b. The rectangle with 42 tiles has a width of 6, and the rectangle with 56 tiles has a width of 8. These answers are found by finding the other number in the factor pair with 7 for each rectangle.

    c. Students' answers will vary. For 42: 1×42, 2×21, or 3×14. For 56: 1×56, 2×28, or 4×14.

3. Jack will only have a conflict one day per month on the 21st. The least common multiple of 3 and 7 is 21. The next common multiple, 42, is greater than the number of days in a month.

4. Since the numbers are prime, they don't have any proper factors. Therefore, their least common multiple would be their product.

5. a. yes   b. yes   c. No; Both numbers have 17 as a factor.

    d. no; Even numbers always have a factor of 2.

6. a. least common multiple: 24; greatest common factor: 4

    b. least common multiple: 105; greatest common factor: 1

    c. least common multiple: 187; greatest common factor: 1

    d. least common multiple: 108; greatest common factor: 36

    e. b and c; In b the two numbers are relatively prime, and in c the two numbers are prime.

Investigation 5

1. a. $630 = 2 \times 3 \times 3 \times 5 \times 7$ b. $144 = 2 \times 2 \times 2 \times 2 \times 3 \times 3$

    c. 101 is prime.   d. $133 = 7 \times 19$

2. a.   b.

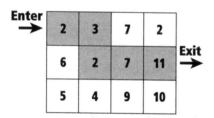

    c.   d.

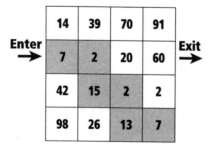

3. a. GCF = 5, LCM = 525   b. GCF = 27, LCM = 81   c. GCF = 9, LCM = 252

4. 105; An odd number cannot have a factor of 2, and 3, 5, and 7 are the only three primes with a product less than 160.

5. **a.** Possible answer: 6 and 36

    b. Possible answer: 12 and 60

    c. The least common multiple is the other number in the pair.

Investigation 6

1. Beginning with the number 3, repeatedly multiply by 3 until the result exceeds 500. The numbers would be 3, 9, 27, 81, 243.

2. **a.** Alternate multiplying terms by 5 and then 2. In other words, multiply the first term by 5 to get the second term, multiply the second term by 2 to get the third, multiply the third term by 5 to get the fourth, multiply the fourth term by 2 to get the fifth, and so on.

    b. 3000 and 15,000

    c. The greatest common factor is 3, since it is the first term in the sequence and a prime number.

3. The largest prime desert less than 50 is {24, 25, 26, 27, 28}.

4. **a.** $23 \times 5 = 115$ **b.** $21 \times 10 = 210$

5. **a.** $190 = 2 \times 5 \times 19$ **b.** $319 = 11 \times 19$ **c.** $255 = 3 \times 5 \times 17$ **d.** $406 = 2 \times 7 \times 29$

abundant number A number with proper factors that add to more than the number. For example, 24 is an abundant number because its proper factors, 1, 2, 3, 4, 6, 8, and 12, add to 36.

common factor A factor that two or more numbers share. For example, 7 is a common factor of 14 and 35 because 7 is a factor of 14 ($14 = 7 \times 2$) and 7 is a factor of 35 ($35 = 7 \times 5$).

common multiple A multiple that two or more numbers share. For example, the first few multiples of 5 are 5, 10, 15, 20, 25, 30, 35, 40, 45, 50, 55, 60, 65, and 70. The first few multiples of 7 are 7, 14, 21, 28, 35, 42, 49, 56, 63, 70, 77, 84, and 91. From these lists we can see that two common multiples of 5 and 7 are 35 and 70.

composite number A whole number with factors other than itself and 1 (i.e., a whole number that is not prime). Some composite numbers are 6, 12, 20, and 1001.

deficient number A number with proper factors that add to less than the number. For example, 14 is a deficient number because its factors, 1, 2, and 7, add to 10. All prime numbers are deficient.

dimensions The dimensions of a rectangle are its length and its width. For example, the rectangle below has width 3 and length 5. We can refer to this rectangle as a 3×5 rectangle.

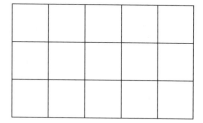

divisor A factor.

even number A multiple of 2. When you divide an even number by 2, the remainder is 0. Examples of even numbers are 2, 4, 6, 8, and 10.

exponent The small raised number that tells how many times a factor is used. For example, 5^3 means $5 \times 5 \times 5$.

factor One of two or more numbers that are multiplied to get a product. For example, 13 and 4 are both factors of 52 because $13 \times 4 = 52$.

Fundamental Theorem of Arithmetic The theory stating that, except for the order of the factors, a whole number can be factored into prime factors in only one way.

multiple The product of a given whole number and another whole number. For example, the first four multiples of 3 are 3, which is 3×1, 6, which is 3×2, 9, which is 3×3, and 12, which is 3×4. Note that if a number is a multiple of 3, then 3 is a factor of the number. For example, 12 is a multiple of 3, and 3 is a factor of 12.

near-perfect number A number with proper factors that add to 1 less than the number. All powers of 2 are near-perfect number. For example, 32 is a near-perfect number because its proper factors, 1, 2, 4, 8, and 16, add to 31.

odd number A whole number that is not a multiple of 2. When an odd number is divided by 2, the remainder is 1. Examples of odd numbers are 1, 3, 5, 7, and 9.

perfect number A number with proper factors that add to exactly the number. For example, 6 is a perfect number because its proper factors, 1, 2, and 3, add to 6.

prime factorization The longest factor string for a number, composed entirely of prime numbers. For example, the prime factorization of 1001 is $7 \times 11 \times 13$. The prime factorization of a number is unique except for the order of the factors.

prime number A number with only two factors, 1 and the number itself. Examples of primes are 11, 17, 53, and 101.

proper factors All the factors of a number, except the number itself. For example, the proper factors of 16 are 1, 2, 4, and 8.

relatively prime numbers Numbers with no common factors except for 1. For example, 20 and 33 are relatively prime because the factors of 20 are 2, 4, 5, and 10, and 20, while the factors of 33 are 3, 11, and 33.

square number The product of a number with itself. Examples of a square numbers are 9, 25, and 81. A square number of square tiles can be arranged to form a square.

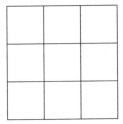

Venn diagram A diagram in which circles are used to show relationships among sets of objects that have certain attributes.

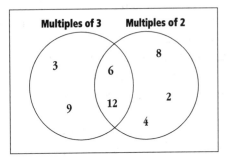

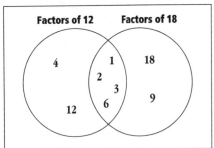

descomposición en factores primos La cadena más larga de factores de un número, compuesta solamente de números primos. Por ejemplo, la descomposición en factores primos de 1001 es $7 \times 11 \times 13$. La descomposición en factores primos de un número es única salvo por el orden de los factores.

diagrama de Venn Un diagrama en el que se usan círculos para representar relaciones entre conjuntos de objetos que tienen ciertos atributos.

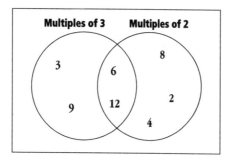

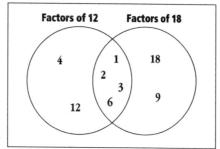

dimensiones Las dimensiones de un rectángulo son su longitud y su ancho. Por ejemplo, el rectángulo representado a continuación tiene un ancho de 3 y una longitud de 5. Podemos referirnos a este rectángulo como a un rectángulo de 3×5.

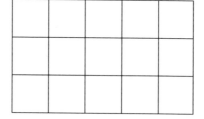

divisor Un factor. Por ejemplo, 5 es factor de 20 porque $5 \times 4 = 20$. Y 5 es divisor de 20 porque la división $20 \div 5$ no tiene resto. Cualquier número que es un factor también es un divisor.

factor Uno de dos o más números que se multiplican para obtener un producto. Por ejemplo, tanto 13 como 4 son factores de 52 porque $13 \times 4 = 52$.

factor común Un factor que es compartido por dos o más números. Por ejemplo, 7 es factor común de 14 y 35 porque 7 es factor de 14 ($14 = 7 \times 2$) y 7 es factor de 35 ($35 = 7 \times 5$).

factores propios Todos los factores de un número salvo el número mismo. Por ejemplo, los factores propios de 16 son 1, 2, 4 y 8.

múltiplo El producto de un número entero dado y otro número entero. Por ejemplo, los primeros cuatro múltiplos de 3 son: 3, que es 3×1; 6, que es 3×2; 9, que es 3×3; y 12, que es 3×4. Observa que si un número es múltiplo de 3, entonces 3 es factor de ese número. Por ejemplo, 12 es múltiplo de 3, y 3 es factor de 12.

múltiplo común un múltiplo compartido por dos o más números. Por ejemplo, los primeros múltiplos de 5 son 5, 10, 15, 20, 25, 35, 40, 45, 50, 55, 60, 65 y 70. Los primeros múltiplos de 7 son 7, 14, 21, 28, 35, 42, 49, 56, 63, 70, 77, 84 y 91. Estas listas nos indican que dos múltiplos comunes de 5 y 7 son el 35 y el 70.

número al cuadrado El producto de un número multiplicado por sí mismo. Ejemplos de números al cuadrado son el 9, el 25 y el 81. Un número al cuadrado representado por baldosas cuadradas puede armarse de manera que forme un cuadrado.

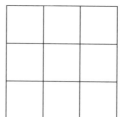

número abundante Un número con factores propios que sumados resultan en un número mayor que el número mismo. Por ejemplo, 24 es un número abundante porque la suma de sus factores propios, 1, 2, 3, 4, 6, 8 y 12, es 36.

número casi perfecto Un número con factores propios que sumados resultan en 1 menos que ese número. Todas las potencias de 2 son números casi perfectos. Por ejemplo, 32 es un número casi perfecto porque sus factores propios 1, 2, 4, 8 y 16 suman 31.

número compuesto Un número entero con otros factores además del número mismo y 1 (es decir, un número entero que no es primo). Algunos números compuestos son 6, 12, 20 y 1001.

número deficiente Un número con factores propios que sumados resultan en un número menor que el número mismo. Por ejemplo, 14 es un número deficiente porque la suma de sus factores 1, 2 y 7 equivale a 10. Todos los números primos son deficientes.

número impar Un número entero que no es múltiplo de 2. Cuando un número impar se divide por 2, el resto es 1. Los siguientes son ejemplos de números impares: 1, 3, 5, 7 y 9.

número par Un múltiplo de 2. Cuando divides un número par por 2, el resto es 0. Los siguientes son ejemplos de números pares: 2, 4, 6, 8 y 10.

número perfecto Un número con factores propios que, cuando se suman, el resultado es ese número exacto. Por ejemplo, 6 es un número perfecto porque la suma de sus factores propios, 1, 2 y 3, es 6.

número primo Un número que tiene sólo dos factores, 1 y sí mismo. Los siguientes son ejemplos de números primos: 11, 17, 53 y 101.

números relativamente primos Números que no tienen factores comunes salvo 1. Por ejemplo, 20 y 33 son números relativamente primos porque los factores de 20 son 1, 2, 4, 5, 10 y 20 mientras que los factores de 33 son 1, 3, 11 y 33. Observa que ni el 20 ni el 33 son en sí mismos números primos.

Teorema fundamental de la aritmética La teoría que enuncia que, salvo por el orden de los factores, un número entero puede descomponerse en factores primos de una sola manera.

Index

Index